Talking About Grammar

R.G. Bowers
B. Bamber
R. Straker Cook
A.L. Thomas

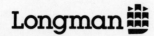

ACKNOWLEDGEMENTS

The authors wish first to acknowledge their debt to Geoffrey Leech and Jan Svartvik both for the wealth of grammatical information in *A Communicative Grammar of English* and for their permission to base *Talking About Grammar* on their work. Secondly, they express gratitude to their students, particularly at the Faculty of Languages and at the Centre for Developing English Language Teaching, Ain Shams University, Cairo, for using and commenting upon earlier versions of this material. Thirdly, they thank family and friends for their patience and good humour during the writing of *Talking About Grammar*. Finally, they are grateful for the insights of Sylvia Chalker.

Longman Group UK Limited
Longman House, Burnt Mill, Harlow,
Essex CM20 2JE, England
and Associated Companies throughout the world

© Longman Group UK Limited 1987

First published 1987

Set in 10/12 pt Times New Roman

Produced by Longman Group (FE) Ltd

Printed in Hong Kong

ISBN 0-582-55899-9

CONTENTS

Each Unit begins with a cross-reference to the relevant paragraphs of *A Communicative Grammar of English*.

INTRODUCTION

This book is based firmly on Leech and Svartvik's *Communicative Grammar of English* (CGE).* It consists of questions (and a key) designed to help teacher and student to dig more deeply into CGE, to find out more about the grammar of English, and to develop a greater awareness of how the communicative potential of English can be exploited.

CGE is designed as a reference book, and it contains a wealth of information on the forms and functions of English. The section with which this workbook is primarily concerned is Part Three: **Grammar in use**. This part of CGE is organised in terms of communicative function, and it will be seen that the units in this workbook follow in general the same order of presentation. In addition, Parts One and Two of CGE refer respectively to **Varieties of English** and to **Intonation**. These two aspects of English in use are also covered fully in this workbook. The fourth part of CGE consists of a **Grammatical Compendium**. Users of this workbook may find it useful to follow up the cross-references to the Grammatical Compendium which they find in Grammar in Use.

A Communicative Grammar of English successfully combines an essentially functional approach to grammar with a comprehensive statement of formal features. It takes full account of variation, including dialectal variation; and it offers descriptions of the spoken form of sentences where this is relevant (as it so often is) to their communicative function and grammatical analysis. CGE has thus established a broad appeal to classroom teachers of many grammatical and pedagogical persuasions.

* Geoffrey Leech and Jan Svartvik, *A Communicative Grammar of English* (Longman 1975)

However, no book designed primarily for personal reference is ideally suited to the needs of the classroom. Supplementary material is normally required which can:

- **select** the information to be discussed in the classroom
- **sequence** that information for pedagogical effectiveness
- **stimulate** the students to seek out and explore the facts for themselves
- **support** the teacher by providing strategies of discussion and explanation as well as a basis for evaluating the students' understanding.

These are the four functions which *Talking About Grammar* fulfils.

The primary objectives of *Talking About Grammar* are thus:

- to develop the language awareness of intermediate and advanced learners
- to improve learners' ability to use CGE as a reference tool
- by exploiting the nature of CGE itself, to convert knowledge of the formal features of English syntax into an understanding of its functions
- to enliven the teaching and learning of English grammar

The design of *Talking About Grammar* allows it to be used both in teacher-taught classes and also by the individual student working alone.

Among those who will find *Talking About Grammar* useful are:

- advanced students of English who need practice material to complement and clarify the explanations and examples in CGE itself
- teachers of advanced learners, particularly in the universities, wherever 'grammar' is a component of the curriculum
- teachers of English eager to develop their own competence
- teacher educators, aiming to develop the language awareness of English teachers-to-be
- non-native and native speaker scholars concerned with the relation between form and function in English
- private students with a special interest in or need for the structures of communication in English

A NOTE TO THE TEACHER

All the questions in *Talking About Grammar* have been trialled in normal classroom use and revised for maximum accuracy, relevance, productivity and attraction. You will find that *Talking About Grammar* brings life to the discussion of grammar in the classroom.

The following procedure is particularly recommended:

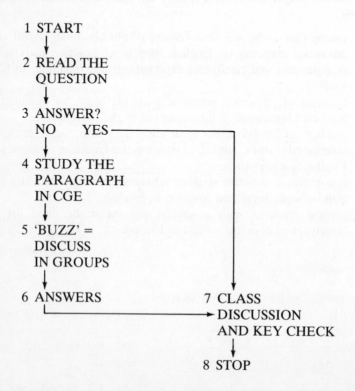

1 START

2 READ THE
  QUESTION

3 ANSWER?
  NO   YES

4 STUDY THE
  PARAGRAPH
  IN CGE

5 'BUZZ' =
  DISCUSS
  IN GROUPS

6 ANSWERS   7 CLASS
                   DISCUSSION
                   AND KEY CHECK

                   8 STOP

1 START

Where you start depends on your needs and interests. Since, in general, questions are sequentially organised with reference to CGE Part Three, **Grammar in use**, you can if you wish start at the first question in the first unit and work through to the last question in the last.

Alternatively, by referring to the paragraph reference on the right of each question, you can jump to the particular point you select.

Be sure, however, that where necessary (particularly in the later units) you are familiar with the discussion of Varieties and Intonation to be found in Parts One and Two of CGE before attempting questions which involve these features.

2 READ THE QUESTION

All questions need to be read carefully. They are intentionally brief, and some are by design elliptical. The enigmatic nature of some questions (which is resolved on reference to the paragraph which is indicated) is in itself a stimulus to personal thought or group discussion. Indeed, it generally helps for students to work together in pairs or small groups from this point on, since the process of discussion itself throws up points of grammar for further exploration.

3 ANSWER?

By all means let students try to answer questions without seeking a solution in CGE: they may already be familiar with the point at issue. In most cases, however, reference to specified paragraphs is required in order to focus on the precise point of grammar in question or to see exactly what response is required. This procedure should be emphasised to the students: the questions are not independent 'tests' of grammatical knowledge so much as stimuli to read the paragraphs of CGE with a particular application in view.

4 STUDY THE PARAGRAPH IN CGE

Allow sufficient time for this, though this will vary from question to question and paragraph to paragraph. Encourage students to scan paragraphs and cross-references (for example, to the **Grammatical Compendium**) as they search for what is relevant.

5 'BUZZ' = DISCUSS IN GROUPS

As has already been emphasised, this is a highly productive part of the procedure, in the course of which students reprocess their reading, offer their solutions, evaluate their own responses, and in so doing cite and use a good deal of language.

6 ANImals

6 ANSWERS
... may be offered by the group or by the individual. Remember that many, perhaps most, questions do not have a single correct answer so much as a range of possible responses. Once again, these are not 'testing' questions but 'teaching' questions: the range of responses which is offered is important in forming the basis for ...

7 CLASS DISCUSSION AND KEY CHECK
Use the questions as an opportunity to probe into the point at issue, to relate back to previous points, to identify areas of misunderstanding or conceptual difficulty, and so to develop the grammatical awareness of your students. Make as much or as little use of the Key as you wish. Sometimes it will help you to focus on the specific point of the question. Often it will give you a sample response. But remember that in many cases a number of responses are possible: do not let the key cramp your imagination! This discussion part of the process should, we suggest, become increasingly difficult to ...

8 STOP!

A NOTE TO THE STUDENT

If you are using this book on your own, remember that you will get little out of it unless you have by your side *A Communicative Grammar of English* and refer to it as directed.

An answer to each question is generally embedded somewhere in CGE. But the questions are not always direct, and in many cases unless you look at the paragraph of CGE which is specified, the answer needed – or even possibly the point of the question – will elude you. Sometimes you may find you have an answer ready: even so, check the CGE paragraph – you will probably find out more than the question itself makes you think of. Remember that this is not a book of test questions: it is a collection of questions designed to help you dig more deeply into CGE and understand more fully the information offered there.

When you have worked out your answer, or if you are in difficulty and need some extra help, turn to the Key for extra advice or confirmation. The Key will not always give you an exact answer because not all the questions have a single correct answer: but it will give you an example, or help you to focus on the precise point of the question.

If you can, work through *Talking About Grammar* from start to finish, and in this way read systematically through CGE. Alternatively, dip in where your fancy leads you – and find out how grammar can be fun!

SYMBOLS

An asterisk (*) signifies that what follows is 'not good English', i.e.
an unacceptable usage: *the car of John.
The symbols < > enclose words which explain varieties of English:
<informal> <polite>.
Other symbols are explained at the beginning of the relevant unit.

UNIT ONE

Talking about things

CGE REFERENCE: CONCEPTS : 47–102

Referring to objects, substances and materials
Abstractions
Amount or quantity
Definite and indefinite meaning
Relations between ideas expressed by nouns
Restrictive and non-restrictive meaning

1	"The government can decide." Is *can* singular or plural?	47
2	"Half a loaf is better than no bread." But would you settle for *a *quarter a loaf*? If not, why not?	48
3	Blades of grass; grains of wheat; . . . . . . of paper; bars of . . . . . .; . . . . . . of rope; planks of . . . . Complete these and think of three more pairs of unit and mass nouns.	49
4	Right or wrong?: (a) an acre of forest; (b) a fathom of wood; (c) a quart of sugar; (d) a ton of flour; (e) a pound of nails; (f) a pint of paint.	50–51
5	This ⎰ type ⎰ of ⎰ weapon ⎰ is ⎰ . . . These ⎰ types ⎰ of ⎰ weapons ⎰ are ⎰ . . . . used in guerrilla warfare. How many acceptable sentences can you make?	52
6	*Watersmeet* is the name of an English village. Where would you expect to find it?	53

7	In some other language, find translations for the words listed in paragraph 55 and say whether they are MASS or COUNT.	55
8	"None of the students were present." Does this mean that some of them were absent?	57
9	"I have few friends." Am I looking on the bright side?	58
10	How much thought do these questions demand?	60
11	"There are ten books. All the books cost ten pounds. Every book costs . . . ." Is there only one answer?	62–63
12	"The election could go either way." How many candidates are there? "Any party could win." How many parties are there?	65
13	"Goats are omnivorous. They'll eat . . . . . . !"	66
14	For some other language, prepare a diagram which shows **scale of amount**.	67–68
15	What are the uses of *the*? Give an example of each.	69–74
16	"Bananas are black." "The bananas are black." Are these sentences acceptable?	76
17	What does an English verb morphology expert specialise in?	77
18	"The . . . . . . get richer and the . . . . . . get poorer." Fill in the blanks.	78
19	"London in the 1940s was . . . . . . London of austerity." Fill in the blank. What about . . . . . . London of the 60s?	81
20	"John met Mary and she killed him. Then Mary met Alice and she killed her." Do we know who survived?	82

21	"It's a boy! And it's just like its father!" "Congratulations! What are you going to call . . . . . .?"	83
22	"If someone were a feminist, he would support equality for women." What would a feminist say about this and the paragraph?	84
23	"And how is our knee today, Mrs Brown?" Whose knee?	85
24	"They say smoking's bad for your health." Who say?	86
25	"That's true, but what about this?" What is *that*, and what is *this*?	88
26	"And now, here is the news." Where is it?	89
27	"I caught this four-pound fish when I was on holiday last year." Isn't it beginning to smell a bit by now?	90
28	Does 'fear of witches' mean that the witches are afraid?	91
29	If a bowl of wood is made of wood, what is a bowl of salad made of?	91
30	One of John's father's brother's son's cousins is . . . . . .?	93
31	"He is obsessed by the hatred of his father." Who hates whom?	93
32	"The company's decision . . ." Did the company decide something? "The company's foundation . . ." Did the company found something?	93
33	Need the girl's story be the story of a girl?	94
34	"The invention of the telephone by Alexander Graham Bell . . ." can be expressed differently. Can you suggest another way?	95
35	"The oldest living person in Egypt's birthday . . ." is not the student's best attempt at composition today. What could he do to improve it?	96

UNIT TWO

Talking about actions and events (I)

CGE REFERENCE: CONCEPTS : 105–139

Time, tense and aspect: states and events; present; past; perfect aspect; state or habit in the past

1	"Leonardo da Vinci was an artist. He painted the Mona Lisa. He also made many scientific discoveries." Talk in the same way about Shakespeare, Cleopatra, Julius Caesar.	105
2	"When *I* use a word," Humpty Dumpty said in a rather scornful tone, "it means just what I choose it to mean – neither more nor less." By *means* does Humpty mean a state or a habit?	106, 108
3	"I declare question three to be the perfect example of a present event verb." Well, is it?	107
4	"I never apologise." said G B Shaw. Is this a sensible habit?	108
5	"Inflation is running at seven per cent." Can you base a long-term forecast on this information?	109
6	"I'm getting good marks these days." Are you sure you can keep it up?	110

22	*"I haven't seen him yesterday." Is there a word missing?	119
23	"I didn't used to like him." Right or wrong?	120
24	"When I was younger, I would climb that tree and . . ." "If I was younger, I would climb that tree and . . ." Which is **wish**, and which was **habit**?	120
25	"So I hit him on the nose and he . . . . . . to the ground." Why can we use either *fell* or *falls*?	121
26	"I hear there's been another earthquake in Antarctica." Are you listening to the live broadcast?	121
27	"I had eggs for breakfast." When?	139 B9
28	"I played tennis." When?	139 B10
29	"He hadn't arrived . . ." Look at time-line B13 and finish the sentence.	139
30	"Hello! I haven't seen you for ages." How, in another language, would you say this?	139 B3

In questions 31–40, give a true example of each time concept. By 'true', we mean a state or event which you have personally either witnessed or experienced.

31	Give a true example of a PRESENT STATE.	106
32	Give a true example of a PRESENT EVENT.	107
33	Give a true example of a PRESENT HABIT.	108
34	Give a true example of a TEMPORARY PRESENT.	109
35	Give a true example of a TEMPORARY HABIT.	110
36	Give a true example of a STATE UP TO THE PRESENT TIME.	115
37	Give a true example of a HABIT UP TO THE PRESENT TIME.	115

UNIT THREE

Talking about actions and events (II)

CGE REFERENCE: CONCEPTS: 122–139

Time, tense and aspect: progressive aspect; future time; future in the past; past in the future

1	"John was just leaving when I called." Did he in fact leave?	122
2	"The audience left when you stood up to speak." Does changing the aspect weaken the criticism?	122
3	"When the lights went out, I . . ." Try to complete this in at least two ways.	122
4	"Whereas the optimist hopes that things are getting better, the pessimist . . . ."	123, 124
5	"The telephone's ringing." If someone says this in a play, what will the stage direction be?	123, 107
6	*"This sentence is looking odd." Why?	124A
7	What do you remember about verbs referring to memory (and other states of mind)?	124B

8	"Are you liking London, Arthur?" Where is Arthur?	124B
9	"These questions need a lot of thought." When, now?	124C
10	"My head feels sore." Is this a permanent disability?	125
11	JENNY: You're looking terrible! PENNY: But I feel well enough. JENNY: You look terrible! PENNY: But I'm feeling well enough. What's wrong?	125
12	"We've been hearing a lot about oil exploration." "We hear a lot about oil exploration." Which sentence could be completed by *from time to time* and which by *recently*?	126
13	"Will you be able to join us next week?" "We . . . . . . so." Express tentative hope.	127
14	Announce the arrival time of the next train from Duncton.	129
15	Look around you, and say what *will* happen *if* . . .	129
16	"There's someone at the door." "All right, I . . . ." Express your intention.	129
17	"He's going to be a lawyer." How do you know?	130
18	"Careful! That saucepan . . ." (They always do when you're not looking!)	130
19	A: Would you like to come round for a drink? B: We're going out. What, this minute?	131
20	"When the plane . . . . . . over Paris, you will see the Seine."	132

21	"I hope the weather isn't too hot." When? Today or tomorrow?	132
22	"When do the exams start this year?" Why *do*?	133
23	"You'll be hearing from my lawyers." Why is the speaker so certain?	134
24	"Well, I'll be going now." Why *will* with *now*?	134
25	"The Prime Minister's making a State visit to China in May." "I am to holiday in Spain this year." Something the wrong way round here?	135
26	"The police were about to move in on the gang when . . ." What happened?	135, 136
27	"Arthur was to regret that morning for the rest of his life." Why is this a useful start to a short story?	136
28	By the time you finish this unit, what will you have achieved?	137
29	"He's doing very well for himself these days." Draw a time-line.	139 A5
30	Make a sentence to suit this time-line:	139 B10
31	"How long have you been waiting here?" Draw a time-line.	139 B5
32	"The lesson starts at one." Is this the most likely time-line?	139 C18
33	"Strachan plays for Scotland." Draw a time-line.	139 A3

34 | Make up a sentence for this time-line:

139
B7

---

35 | "The summit talks are going to be held in Geneva next autumn."

139
C16

Find other ways of saying the same thing with the same time-line.

36 | "We'll have passed out by the time the waiter brings the soup!"
Draw a time-line.

139
C21

37 | "I had worked hard for my promotion."
Does this time-line fit this sentence?

139
B13

38 | "I had only seen the play once before."
Draw a time-line.

139
B12

39 | Which time-line fits this sentence:
"I sentence you to three years' imprisonment."

139
A2

40 | "I've answered these questions with growing confidence."
Assuming that you have, draw a time-line!

139
B3

UNIT FOUR

Talking about time

CGE REFERENCE: CONCEPTS: 140–160

Time-when
Duration
Frequency

1	"When did you last fill up with petrol?" Answer in at least five ways.	140
2	"If yesterday was Sunday, then tomorrow . . . ." "Ah, but it was Saturday yesterday, so Tuesday . . . ."	140

Take the next three questions together.
Use prepositions!

3	What time is sunset today?	141
4	Which day do you normally take a break from the weekly routine?	141
5	When are your favourite flowers in bloom?	141
6	"Industry has exerted a strong influence on social structure in the last century." How many words can you find to replace *in*?	141
7	"The doctor is available for consultation . . . . . . five . . . . . . seven pm daily." Complete in two ways.	141

8 | "Nostalgia isn't what it used to be!"   142
Talk about your childhood, mostly using *during*.

9 | Plan a month's holiday in Britain. Describe week by week the places   142
you will visit, where you will stay, and what you will do.

10 | Describe what you intend to do over the next three days.   143

11 | "How did you avoid the heat?"   143
"We travelled . . . ."

12 | "This year, next year, sometime, never." is a popular children's   144
jumping and skipping song.
Express your own plans and hopes for the future: you won't need
many prepositions.

13 | "Send the telex on . . . ."   144
"Can't be done."
"Why not?"
"The office is closed . . . ."
Sunday, or Sundays?

14 | If you last met John two weeks ago, when did you last meet John?   144
Use two *last*s in your answer!

15 | Two English expressions for you: 145
"Look *before* you leap!"
"Don't count your chickens *before* they're hatched."
Make up some more, using *before*.

16 | When do you think you will have finished this book by?   145

17 | The train leaves at twelve. It travels at about 45 miles an hour,   145
and the distance is just under 350 miles. What time should
it arrive?

18 | "Give me your answer sheet."   145
"But . . ."
Protest in two ways, using *already* and *yet*.

19 | "How long does it take to drive from London to Edinburgh?"   146
"Well, it's 400 miles, but as it's a good road all the way there, you can
do it . . ."
How good is your mental arithmetic?

20	How would you translate the phrases in the paragraph into another language?	147
21	"My doctor says I must go back for a complete check-up." "When?" Answer in three different ways using MEASURE PHRASES.	148
22	"I arrived fifteen minutes early for the film, and Marilyn arrived ten minutes later." Did she see the beginning?	148
23	"When did we last have the house painted?" "Two years . . . ." "When shall we have it painted again?" "Two years . . . ."	148
24	"He's just coming." "He's just come." Does *just* mean the same thing?	149
25	"He has since apologised." Since what?	149
26	"The audience stood up . . . . . . the National Anthem started." Look at the paragraph and find three ways of completing the sentence.	150
27	"When did you enter the country?" *"While we are arguing about my visa, I reckon."* "I see, and how long did you stay in Cairo?" *"On March the fourth."* "And when did you visit Luxor?" *"Since the fourth of March."* "So how long have you been staying in Egypt?" *"Over the weekend."* "And when does your plane leave?" *"For three weeks."* Help the tourist and the immigration official to sort themselves out: it's the tourist who's muddled up!	151–1!
28	Look up the word *insomnia* in your dictionary. Now describe the habits of an insomniac, using (and not using) *for*.	152
29	"Sebastian was in the lead up to the last moment." Who won the race?	153

UNIT FIVE

Talking about place

CGE REFERENCE: CONCEPTS: 161–191

Place, direction and distance

Many of the questions in this unit refer to the map of the (imaginary) town Duncton, which you will find on page 19.
If you see an arrow (→) in the reference column, you can only answer the question by looking at the map.

1	"Where are you working at the moment?" Look at the paragraph and answer truthfully in four ways.	161
2	Using the paragraph, describe four things you did on a weekend trip to Duncton.	163 →
3	Guided by the paragraph, describe an imaginary drive around Duncton.	164 →
4	Can you look across a window?	165
5	"We walked into the park." "We walked in the park." Any difference?	166
6	You went for a walk in Duncton on a cold and windy day. Using the paragraph, describe the weather and your walk.	167 →
7	How many places can you find to eat within fifty metres of the hotel?	168 →

8	Where can you park your car in Duncton?	169 →
9	Using the paragraph and your imagination, describe the hotel.	170 →
10	"This bus stops at Duncton." Is it a long-distance or a local bus?	171
11	Why is Christopher Columbus famous? What about Marco Polo?	172
12	Where does the Mayor of Duncton work? (Try mentioning the town, the building and the street it's in.)	173 →
13	What did the angry policeman do when you jumped the lights? "He shouted . . . . . . me!"	174
14	You had a picnic in the park, and then went for a row. What did you sit on, and then in?	175
15	As you row your boat along the river, what do you see and where?	176 →
16	Where would you find a crypt?	176, 177
17	How does a colour-blind man obey the traffic-lights?	176
18	You have left your car keys in the hotel room. Call your wife or husband and describe exactly where they are.	176
19	"The river flows . . . . . . the bridge." "There's deep water . . . . . . the bridge." Under? Underneath? Beneath? Below?	177
20	Using the paragraph, say where the pubs are in Duncton.	178 →
21	When you travel by car, do you like to sit in front? In front of what?	179
22	"The owl looked up to the stars . . . . . . And sang to a small guitar, 'O lovely pussy! O pussy my . . . . . ., What a beautiful pussy you are!' " Fill in these lines by Edward Lear. Make them rhyme!	179

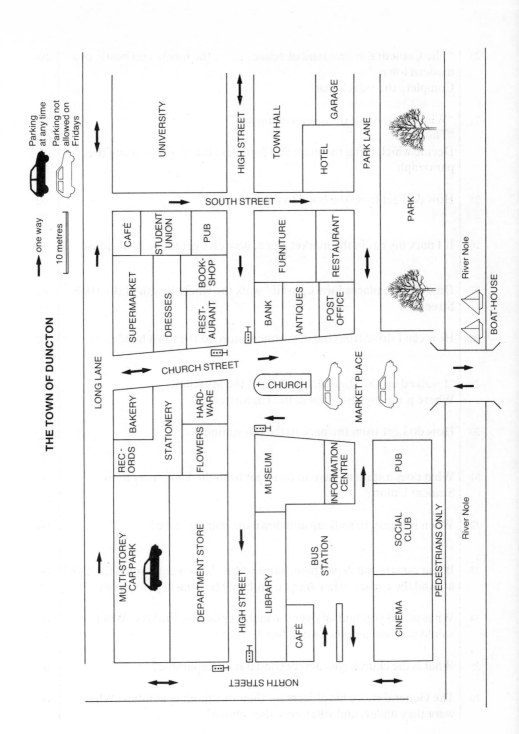

THE TOWN OF DUNCTON

23 | "The Cathedral is an island of peace . . . . . . the hustle and bustle of a modern town."
Complete the travelogue. | 180

24 | "Which restaurant do you recommend?"
"The one . . . ."
Decide which using the map, and complete the response using the paragraph. | 180
→

25 | How do I get from the hotel to the post office? | 181
→

26 | If I park my car in the market place, how do I get to the boat-house? | 181
→

27 | Describe the places I walk *past* if I walk the whole length of the High Street. | 182
→

28 | How can I drive from the department store to the town hall? | 182
→

29 | "I walked up the High Street towards the Museum."
Where is the highest point in the High Street? | 183

30 | How do I get from the park to the bus station? | 183
→

31 | What does a student have to do to get from the University to the Student Union? | 183
→

32 | When is it easy to walk up and down the market place? | 184
→

33 | If you can see the department store across the road and smell the café around the corner, what are you probably holding in your hands? | 185
→

34 | What would you find all over the market place on Fridays? What would you find on other weekdays? | 187
→

35 | What is the church past and beyond if it is irreparable? | 188

36 | The General chose his officers for their outstanding abilities. What were they under, and what were they above? | 188

37 | What's the first thing I do when I arrive in Duncton by bus – even before I look at the map? | 189

38 | Using the paragraphs and the map, describe in detail a bank robbery. | 189, 190 →

39 | "The railway tunnel runs a thousand metres . . . . . . the mountain." Try using *through* and *under*, and say what change of meaning occurs. | 191, 176, 181

40 | What expressions would you use in another language to label the five basic spatial concepts? | 162

UNIT SIX

How and why, if and whether

CGE REFERENCE: CONCEPTS: 192–216

Manner, means and instrument
Cause, reason and purpose
Condition and contrast

1	How were the pyramids built? Using the paragraph, answer in three ways.	192
2	How do I dress if I share your fashion sense?	193
3	Sailors like a job to be done 'shipshape and Bristol fashion', that is to say, 'in . . . . . .'.	193
4	Can you explain how to put on a tie, or hold a baby, or peel a banana? (Don't use your hands!)	193
5	"He smokes too much." "I'll say," I replied conversationally. "He smokes . . . ." Provide the analogy.	194
6	"She's rather condescending, don't you think?" "Well, yes," I said guardedly. "She does speak to me as if . . ."	194
7	Answer this question . . . . . . referring to the paragraph. (How well you answer will depend on the preposition you use!)	195

8	"I always eat peas with honey, I've done it all my life. They do taste kind of funny, But it keeps them on the knife." What, apart from honey, do I eat my peas with?	195
9	How do you keep in touch with distant friends?	196
10	Make a sentence where an actor is the active ACTOR.	197
11	Make a passive sentence where a secret agent is the AGENT.	198
12	Why do people climb mountains? Answer using the paragraph.	199
13	The match was cancelled $\begin{cases} \text{because of the weather.} \\ \text{.....................} \end{cases}$ The footballer missed the match $\begin{cases} \text{because he was injured.} \\ \text{.....................} \end{cases}$ Using the paragraph, find two paraphrases to fill each gap.	199
14	How does a 'self-made' man succeed?	200
15	What will happen if you put boiling water into a glass?	201
16	"Human history," H G Wells said, "becomes more and more a race between education and catastrophe." Discuss what education brings about, and what lack of education leads to.	201
17	Which came first, the chicken or the egg? Explain this ovoid circularity!	202
18	Why are there no chickens in Kentucky?? ".............., so ...."	202
19	Why did the chicken cross the road???	203
20	"Why did the accused kill his wife?" Using the paragraph, find bad motives for the prosecution, and good ones for the defence. (You give your sexist prejudices full rein at your own peril!)	203

21	You have suddenly decided to do lots of exercise. Using the paragraph, give your reasons.	204
22	You are now in hospital. What were the consequences of your new exercise routine? "I .... and ...."	204
23	"Now that micro-computers have become cheaper, they are in great demand." Rephrase this more <formally>.	205
24	Name three famous people, and say what they are famous for.	206
25	Complete this formal notification: "We have not received your subscription for the current year. We are ...... obliged to ...."	207
26	Complete the sentence: "A trapeze artist hopes he will never use the safety net, but it gives him confidence to know that it is there ..."	208
27	"If I took a driving test, I ..." What's the most likely ending to this sentence? Is the speaker expecting to take his driving test at present?	208
28	"You can borrow this book ...... you promise to return it." Complete, using the paragraph.	209
29	 ┌─────────────────────────┐ │ BREAK GLASS │ │ .... │ │ .... │ └─────────────────────────┘ Complete the emergency instructions with four words.	209
30	You need to look up the reference on the right. Why?	210
31	"Luckily, the crash barrier prevented the car from plunging into the river." We might also say: "...... the crash barrier, the driver would have drowned."	210
32	"Come and stay with me when you visit London." Can you make this rather more tentative?	211

33 | "Although these questions are short, they are difficult." | 212
How would you say this in another language?

34 | You crashed your car in question 31. You are still fit and well. Using | 212
the paragraph, contrast the seriousness of the accident with your state
of health.

35 | You have to give a speech in public: this is something you are | 213
unaccustomed to. How might you begin your speech?

36 | "Dai Jones fell and twisted his ankle a mile from the end of the | 214
Marathon. He went on to win the race."
Using the paragraph, suggest several ways in which a journalist could
report this for the Sports Page.

37 | "Did he pass his driving test?" | 214
"Pass it? He didn't . . . . . . it!"

38 | "What does a gate-crasher do?" | 215
"He goes to parties . . . ."

39 | "Whether the weather is cold | 216
Or whether the weather is hot
We'll weather the weather
Whatever the weather
. . . . . . we like it . . . . . .!"

40 | "With rings on her fingers | 216
And bells on her toes
She shall have music
. . . ."
Complete the rhyme for this ubiquitous lady.

UNIT SEVEN

Just like, better than, and so on

CGE REFERENCE: CONCEPTS: 217–243

Degree
Role, standard and viewpoint
Comparison
Addition, exception and restriction
Subject matter: *about* **and** *on*

1	How much are you enjoying this work? (Use the paragraph: you don't have to be honest.)	217A
2	Now emphasise how much you enjoy grammar!	217B
3	"How old can a young man be before he is middle-aged?"	218
4	"It's quite likely that he's absolutely half-witted." Is this speaker a little careless in his use of English, or utterly slovenly?	219, 220, 224
5	How would you feel if you inherited a large amount of money?	219A
6	<Informally>, describe some recent rises in the cost of living.	219B
7	Give some examples in another language of degree types A, B and C in the paragraph. Compare them with equivalent expressions in English.	219

8	Do you find all this virtually incomprehensible, or utterly confusing? (Be absolutely honest!)	220
9	If the news was fairly surprising, was it quite remarkable?	219, 220
10	How can I send you more than my good wishes? How can I send you even more than that?	221
11	Using the paragraph, give a list of your likes and preferences.	222
12	"Is my bath ready?" "The water's rather hot." Is the bath ready?	223
13	Someone has stolen your CGE. How angry are you?	224
14	How, in another language, would you say 'very large' and 'absolutely massive'?	224
15	What is an almost inaudible noise?	225
16	"Because the roof . . . . . . needed repairing, he worked . . . . . . to mend it, but he . . . . . . enjoyed the task." Try *hard, thoroughly, badly*.	226
17	What are *you* good at? Using the paragraph, describe some of your best ROLES. For modesty's sake, limit one or two of them by mentioning a STANDARD.	227
18	In what senses is television good and bad for society? "It's good in that . . .; but . . ."	228
19	"Jack is more careful than Jill." How else might we say this?	229
20	In another language, describe in as many ways as you can the picture in the paragraph.	229
21	Using the paragraph, compare this book with another one.	229
22	Using different forms of comparison: – compare aluminium with lead and lead with gold. – compare aluminium, lead and gold. – compare half a pound of iron with eight ounces of feathers.	231

23	For the record, describe: Mount Everest, the Nile, the Pacific, the Soviet Union, China, Tokyo, English.	231
24	What's happening to the cost of living?	233
25	Why is Antarctica uninhabited? (Use the paragraph.)	234
26	Look back at question 12 and ask if the bath is ready. (The water should have cooled down by now.)	234
27	How, in another language, would you say: "The tea is too hot for me to drink."	234
28	Manhattan is covered with skyscrapers because . . .	235
29	How, in another language, would you say: "She's such a nice girl!"	235
30	"A Pyrrhic victory means less of a . . . . . . than a . . . ." Or, to put it another way, ... a defeat . . . . . . a victory.	236
31	"The sooner we start, . . ."	237
32	Tell us, in four different ways, what other subjects you are studying. Try using not only prepositions but also adverbials.	238
33	What can an ambidextrous person do?	238
34	Using the paragraph, talk about wood, oil, water, floating and sinking. Be positive and negative.	239
35	Hector is the best player in the team. Achilles is the second best player. So Achilles is the best player	240
36	"Goats will eat anything – . . . ." Express your surprise by using examples.	240

37

> MEMBERS ONLY
> OPEN 9–7
> NO PLAY ON SUNDAYS
> COURTS MUST BE
> BOOKED IN ADVANCE

Using the paragraph, write out the restrictions in full.

38 | For a perfectionist, ... the . . . . . . is good enough.

241

39 | "My daughter also studies French."
As well as my son, or as well as Italian?

242

40 | "I thought of you and smiled."
"I thought about you and smiled."
Which is the more flattering?

243

UNIT EIGHT

Giving information and expressing opinions

**CGE REFERENCE: INFORMATION, REALITY AND BELIEF:
244–277**

Statements, questions and responses
Omission of information
Reported statements and questions
Denial and affirmation

Note that in this unit (and others which follow) you must pay careful
attention to the intonation wherever it is marked for you. You will
find a guide to intonation markings in **Part Two** of your CGE.

1 | JOHN: Who am I?
What, unless he is playing a party game, is odd about John's
question? | 244

2 | GERT: Are these the ones you bought for me?
BERT: No, they're not the ones I bought for you.
Is Bert wasting his breath? | 245

3 | ANGUS: Have you ever been to Edinburgh?
WILLIE: I'm going to Manchester tomorrow.
Give two reasons why this is not the most natural response. | 245

4 | "Would you like cáke, púdding, jélly, frúit ...?"
Is that the end of the list? | 246

5	"Will you hélp me?" "Will you hélp me, or nòt?" What's the difference?	246
6	"Have you . . . . . . information about the robbery?" Does it matter whether we put *some* or *any* in the blank?	248
7	"Would you like . . . . . . help?" What is the difference between *some* and *any* here?	248
8	"You haven't seen the fílm?" What is the speaker assuming?	249
9	"You're not húngry then?" Is your friend likely to agree? If so, how will she show it?	249
10	"The blossom's bèautiful, ísn't it?" What's odd about this?	250
11	". . . . . . you think you're clèver, dó you?" Shouldn't the question tag be negative? Which little word in the blank would help to clarify things?	250
12	"Aren't you in béd yet?" When might you ask this question?	251
13	"How, when and where will you send them?" Answer this question in a maximum of six words.	252, 245
14	"Could you tell me where the station is?" "Where's the station?" Does it make any difference which we say?	253
15	When would I say "Yés?" instead of "Yès."? (This ought to ring a bell!)	254
16	EDWARD: I don't like it there. TED: . . . . . .? EDWARD: At the North Pole. TED: . . . . . .? EDWARD: Because it's too cold. Complete the dialogue.	255

17	ROSE: It's twenty past seven. VIOLET: . . . . . . ROSE: Twenty past seven. Complete the dialogue in as many ways as possible.	256, 257
18	"Sórry?" What am I sorry for?	258
19	"Absolùtely." If this is the only word I say, what has the previous speaker said?	259
20	"FRAGILE" If we see this single word written on a label, what is fragile?	260, 262
21	"Want to try it?" "Wouldn't mind." Who might want to try it, and who wouldn't mind?	261
22	*"Let's go home," suggested he. If it's all right for Tom, Dick or Harry, why isn't it all right for him?	264
23	Horace suggested deciding it there and then. What words did Horace actually use?	265
24	"I should be glad if you won," he said. He said he would be glad if I won. "I should stop smoking," he said. He said he should stop smoking. Why *should*? Why *would*?	266
25	"Fish is good for you," George maintained. George maintained that fish is good for you. Why *is*?	266
26	"I've never had such fun," she laughed. *She laughed that she had never had such fun. What makes this unacceptable?	266
27	I asked him if he liked cheese. What did I actually say?	267
28	"Is it John's or Mary's?" asked Fred. What did Fred want to know?	268

29	How, in another language, do people report speech?	264–268
30	"She definitely won't win." "She won't definitely win." In which case might she win?	269
31	"Jemima didn't eat any of the food." "Jessica didn't eat some of the food." Who ate what, if anything?	270
32	"Travelling such long distances is not unusual in America or Australia." Do Americans and Australians often travel long distances?	271
33	"But he has broken his leg." When would we place the emphasis like this?	272
34	"So you didn't know the answer." What had I previously assumed?	273
35	FRANK: Words should not be repeated unnecessarily. ERNEST: I agree that words should not be repeated unnecessarily. Help Ernest to avoid the redundancy.	274
36	"No, I don't." Is this the answer to a question?	275
37	UNCLE: Charlie's a bit of a fool. AUNT: I would have said he was rather intelligent. Why is it that Aunt *would have* said it when she *already has* said it?	276
38	"New York is the capital of America." <Tactfully> correct the speaker.	276
39	"She made the dress not for herself, . . ." What's the next word?	277, 273
40	You are *not* rich. You *are* healthy. Deny your wealth and affirm your good fortune.	277

UNIT NINE

Putting a point of view

CGE REFERENCE: INFORMATION, REALITY AND BELIEF:
278–302

Agreement and disagreement
Fact, hypothesis and neutrality
Degrees of likelihood
Attitudes to truth

1	"No, you're <u>wrong</u>." What's wrong with saying this?	278
2	"Yes, I'm afraid he is." What is the speaker expressing?	279
3	"......, I couldn't agree with that." "......, I couldn't agree more." Yes? No?	279
4	"Quite right." "Quite good." What does *quite* mean? Quite an easy question? Are you quite sure?	279, 219
5	"Yès." "Y̌es." Do both these indicate total agreement?	280
6	"America is so different from Britain." "It's true that the differences are quite noticeable, but . . ." Complete the partial agreement.	281

7	"Actually, I would go further . . ." Go further.	282
8	"I wish I had done it when I had the chance." Did I do it?	283
9	"I'm surprised he agreed." Did he agree?	284
10	"If I had a hammer . . ." (as the song goes). Hypothesis or fact? Past, present or future?	284
11	A: What time is it? B: Time you had a watch! What does B know about A?	285
12	"What if they had discovered the truth?" Did they? "What if they discovered the truth?" Will they?	285, 284
13	"I wouldn't do that if I were you." Who am I?	286A
14	"If more jobs are threatened, we shall have to go on strike." Rephrase your union's reaction to rising unemployment in more formal terms.	286 B, C
15	"Should there be any change in the regulations, we shall inform you." Friend, or lawyer?	287
16	Is a sentence beginning with "Had they . . ." necessarily a question?	287
17	Is a sentence beginning with "Hadn't they . . ." necessarily a question?	287
18	"I hope to see her again." Will I see her again or not?	288
19	*"I wonder that he will come." Why can't we say this?	288
20	"Did she tell you that she was married?" "Did she tell you whether she was married?" What is in doubt in each case?	288

34	"Boys will be boys." When?	300
35	(Door bell rings.) "That will be David again." When?	300
36	"Sidney should be in Paris by now." Is the speaker sure that Sidney is in Paris?	301
37	What are you not certain about if you have doubts about someone's honesty?	304
38	"I believe Patience was ill yesterday." "In my opinion Patience was ill yesterday." Is there any difference between these two remarks?	305
39	"Do all birds fly?" Express your opinion.	306
40	What expressions, in another language, show the speaker's attitudes to the truth of what he says?	302

UNIT TEN

Saying what you feel

CGE REFERENCE: MOOD, EMOTION AND ATTITUDE: 309–339

Emotive emphasis in speech
Describing emotions
Volition

1	What does / ɑ: / mean? What does / oʊ / mean?	309
2	How would you express sudden pain in another language?	309
3	"How hot is the sun" "How hot the sun is" What punctuation is needed here?	310
4	"Please don't shout so." What does *so* really mean?	311
5	Is this book very boring, or very very boring?	312
6	"She did do it." "She did it." What's the difference?	313
7	"Jacques is a terrific cook." "Jules is a terrible cook." Whose restaurant would you rather eat at?	315

8	"The weather was awful." "The weather was awfully nice." What does *awful* mean? What about *awfully*?	315
9	"I mean it." Add one word for emphasis.	315
10	"What on earth are you doing?" "What are you doing on earth?" The same thing?	316
11	Distinguish between: "Where did you see her?" "Wherever did you see her?"	316
12	"What a miser! He didn't give the beggar . . . ." Complete.	317
13	"He can't possibly get there in time." "Possibly he can't get there in time." What does *possibly* mean?	318
14	"'Was 'he a̍ngry" How would you punctuate this?	319
15	Why do teachers use rhetorical questions? Is it because they know all the answers?	320
16	"Who cares?" Do I really want an answer to this question?	320
17	"To be or not to be; that is the question." What is the question?	320
18	"He was often angry with his friends." Were he and his friends angry together?	321
19	NEIL: I was . . . . see you at our party. MARGARET: I was . . . . come. Using the paragraph, complete this friendly exchange.	321
20	Find the 'odd man out' in this list: fortunately, cheerfully, amazingly, happily, regrettably, luckily, strangely.	323

21	"He loves acting." "He loves to act." What is the difference?	324
22	Do *like* and *enjoy* function in exactly the same way?	324
23	*"We prefer buses better than trains." How would you prefer to phrase this sentence?	325
24	"We will meet at midnight." Be hopeful about your tryst.	327
25	"I'm really looking forward to it." Is it good or bad?	328
26	"If only I'd known!" Did I know then? And how do I feel now?	329
27	Express your (undoubted) approval of this book. Use an exclamation mark!	330
28	"I don't think of Doris much." "I don't think much of Doris." What would Doris think of these two comments?	331
29	"Do you really need to have the music so loud?" Is this really a question?	331
30	How do you express surprise in another language?	332
31	"Jeremy was wearing odd shoes." "How . . . . . .!" Express your surprise.	332
32	What does *I will* mean? (Think about marriage certificates rather than death certificates!)	335
33	"Jasper is so mean he . . . . . . cross the road to pick up a secondhand bus ticket!" *Will* or *would*?	335
34	"I wish, I wish, I were a fish." Express some other impossible desires.	336

35 | Does "Do you want . . ." mean "Would you like . . ."? | 337

36 | "If only I had ten pounds!"
"Only if I had ten pounds."
Find two contexts to show the difference. | 337

37 | "Let's dance."
Put your invitation somewhat less abruptly. | 337

38 | "Tom means to make amends."
"To compensate means to make amends."
What does *mean* mean? | 338

39 | "I've made up my mind and I . . . . . . to stick to my decision." | 338

40 | "He will keep talking."
When? Where should the emphasis be placed? | 339

UNIT ELEVEN

Making friends and influencing people

CGE REFERENCE: MOOD, EMOTION AND ATTITUDE: 340–365

Permission and obligation
Influencing people
Friendly communications
Vocatives

1	"Can your son swim?" Is this remark ambiguous?	340, 296
2	"Might I ask what you're doing here?" When might I? "Might he ask what we're doing here?" When might he?	340, 293
3	"Would you mind my opening a window?" Leave out *my*. What difference does this make?	340, 349
4	"You must be home by twelve o'clock." Who might say this to whom on what occasion?	341
5	"I must go now." "I've got to go now." Do these mean the same?	341

6	"You have to drive on the right." Does this mean: "I order you to drive on the right." or: "You are required by regulations to drive on the right."	341
7	"Need you leave so soon?" *"Yes, I need." What's wrong with this?	342
8	"I must invite the Jacksons to dinner." Will I? "I ought to invite the Jacksons to dinner." Will I?	343
9	"You'd better study hard, $\left\{ \begin{array}{l} \text{or} \dots \text{"} \\ \text{if} \dots \text{"} \end{array} \right.$ Fill the gaps.	343
10	"You mustn't stand in the bath while switching the light on." "You needn't stand in the bath while switching the light on." Same or different?	344, 342
11	Think of a command beginning with "You are . . .".	345
12	Think of a command beginning with a preposition.	345(a)
13	Think of a command consisting of an adverb.	345(a)
14	"ALL MEMBERS WILL OBSERVE THE REGULATIONS OF THE CLUB." Is this a prediction?	345(b)
15	"Don't say a word to anyone." Who mustn't say a word?	346
16	When is a command not a command? When it's an invitation! Try some examples.	346
17	"Make sure you arrive on time." Soften this in three ways.	347
18	How, in another language that you know, can you <tactfully> get someone to do something for you?	348

19	"Lend me a fiver till Tuesday." is very < informal >! Now be < polite >: ". . . a few pounds until my cheque arrives." Now be < formal >: ". . . £2000 to finance this exciting new project."	349
20	Offer someone the same piece of advice, first with an expression beginning with "You . . ." and then with an expression beginning with "I . . .".	350
21	"I suggest you ask him." You might try saying this differently.	350
22	"Let's go home." "Let us go home." One of these remarks is ambiguous. How?	350
23	"Why don't we have dinner together tonight?" John said. Report John.	350
24	CLEOPATRA: Are you doing anything tomorrow evening? ANTONY: No, I'm not. CLEOPATRA: Would you like to come for dinner then? How can Antony refuse?	351
25	What has Cleopatra just done?	352
26	"The vicar was dissuaded from declining the invitation to open the village fete." Did he open the fete or not?	354
27	"Eat one more of those and you'll be sick." Rephrase the warning, using "If . . .".	355
28	What do warnings, promises and threats have in common?	355
29	"I'll come and see you when you're feeling better," Fred said. "So will I," said Ned. You like Fred. You don't like Ned. Report what they said.	356
30	"Helló. . . . Oh, hellò." What is happening here?	358

31	"Good night, Herbert. How are you?" Is there anything unusual about this remark?	358
32	If "This is Ariadne Waterbottle." functions as an introduction, what does "This is an inflatable elephant." function as?	358
33	"How are you getting on?" Getting on what?	359
34	"Yours faithfully," "Yours sincerely," What do you offer unknown businessmen – faith or sincerity?	360
35	In English, do you invariably respond to thanks? What about other languages you know?	361
36	"Remember me?" "Remember me to George." What is the meaning of *remember*?	362
37	"Congratulations on your birthday." Is there anything unusual about this? Is there a more favoured expression?	362
38	ROB: Would you like some more coffee? BOB: Thank you. Would Bob get his coffee? Now try this in another language that you know.	363
39	"Father, we want you to marry us." Explain the context!	364

40	How would you address the following, (a) in English, (b) in another language that you know?
	    (1) a waiter
	    (2) a friend
	    (3) a teacher
	    (4) a judge
	    (5) a customer
	    (6) a public audience
	    (7) the man next door who plays his music too loud
		364,
		365

UNIT TWELVE

Putting it all together

CGE REFERENCE: MEANINGS IN CONNECTED DISCOURSE: 368–389

Linking signals
Linking constructions
'General purpose' links

7	"He's not interested in the job; . . . . . ., he wouldn't be suitable even if he were." Fill the gap.	371
8	What sort of expressions are used to reinforce arguments in another language that you know?	371
9	"The TV programmes are lousy tonight." Reinforce your reluctance to watch TV by declaring that the TV is broken.	371
10	"All in all, we had a splendid holiday." Could this begin a conversation?	372
11	"Edna is witty, intelligent and beautiful; in short, a perfect companion." Am I complaining about Edna's height?	372
12	"Hardworking. Perceptive. Well liked. Well turned out. . . . . . ., a credit to the school." Complete this end-of-year report.	372
13	"In a word, there is no possible way in which I can accede to your request." Make the speaker true to his word.	372
14	"Cats are very self-sufficient animals. . . . . . ., they can perfectly well look after themselves."	373
15	Where are you likely to find *viz.*, and how is it used?	373
16	What words are used in another language that you know to indicate that an expansion or clarification of meaning is to follow?	373
17	"My daughter is very happy at school, or . . . . . . I think she is." Complete the comment.	374
18	"Fleming invented penicillin, ... he discovered it. . . . . . ., he identified a natural substance." Fill the gaps to be precise.	374
19	In what way does *meanwhile* link two or more situations?	375
20	What does the word *nevertheless* tell us about a speaker's next words?	376

21	*"Although he was ill, but he attended his class." In one of two ways, make the sentence acceptable.	376
22	"It was the very first time that Humphrey was going to jump out of an aeroplane, but he was nevertheless terrified." Do you find anything unusual about this?	376
23	"When Gertrude returned home, her mother was very happy." "Gertrude returned home and her mother was very happy." What does the speaker assume the hearer knows in each case?	377
24	"He took a deep breath and then dived into the cold lake." Does *then* make any difference?	378, 379
25	"He counted to ten. He leapt clear of the plane. He pulled the ripcord. He put his parachute on." Hang on, let's get this right.	379
26	The pilot in the last question got the order wrong. Describe the unfortunate results.	380
27	MONA: I've got a headache because I'm taking these pills. JONAH: I'm taking these pills because I've got a headache. Do Mona and Jonah suffer from the same symptoms?	380
28	"An apple a day keeps the doctor away." Rephrase the proverb using *if*.	381
29	"However, we have many problems." "However many problems we have . . ." How does *however* relate to preceding and following ideas in these examples?	383, 376
30	"Mavis is not only a child." "Mavis is not an only child." Which sentence implies addition, and which multiplication?	384
31	What is a working wife? "A woman who, ..., ..."	384
32	"We can go to a concert. We can go to the cinema." Use either *either . . . or* or *or else* to link the alternatives.	385

33	"Hubert went out and bought a hat." "Hubert went out in the rain and got wet." What function does *and* perform in each case?	386
34	"My husband is a comedian, and that's no joke!" Rephrase using a relative!	387
35	"He rode all the way on a camel which was not very sensible." What does *which* refer to?	387
36	"Anyone who ill-treats children should be punished." Rephrase to stress **time-when**. Then rephrase to stress **condition**.	387
37	"Being an actor, . . ." How important is the comma here?	388
38	"Fried, the meat would have been delicious." Was it fried? Was it delicious?	388, 284
39	"He gazed at the poor girl, too embarrassed to speak." Who was embarrassed? Make it clearer.	388
40	"Don't drink that water; you'll be ill." What is the implied connection?	389

UNIT THIRTEEN

Keeping it short

CGE REFERENCE: MEANINGS IN CONNECTED DISCOURSE: 390–409

Substitution and omission

1	"Charlie was wearing a life-jacket. Charlie was saved." Rescue this from repetition without losing any of the meaning.	390
2	"Leo's father was angry because he'd lost his new pen." Whose pen? Who lost it? How do you know?	391
3	"You and . . . . . . should pool . . . . . . resources." Complete the sentence in two ways.	392
4	"Anyone who doesn't do their homework will be punished." Is this acceptable?	393
5	"The Zygian public have made known their decision." "The Zagian public has made known its decision." Which announcement stresses the group response, and which the individual within the group?	393
6	A: Would you like a cup of tea? B: Yes, I'd love . . . . A: Would you like milk? B: Yes, I'd love . . . . Complete the two responses.	394

7	"What sort of sugar would you like in your coffee, the white one or the brown one?" Is this acceptable?	395
8	*"Was she wearing a green dress, or a blue?" Why is this unacceptable?	395
9	"Both dresses were nice, but . . . . . . with the belt was prettier than the other one." Fill the blank with one word.	397
10	"Country houses are often quieter than . . . . . . in the city." Fill the blank with one word.	397
11	"The climate of the desert is drier than the climate of the jungle." Don't repeat yourself.	397
12	"Peter can play as well as Horace does." What happens if we take out *does*?	398, 384
13	TOM: Who wants a drink? DICK: Me. HARRY: I. Whose answer is more appropriate, Dick's or Harry's?	398
14	HERO: Why don't you go swimming? LEANDER: I . . . . . ., regularly. Supply one word to show that Hero's assumption was wrong.	398
15	"I'll complain if you complain." Don't repeat yourself.	399
16	Horace said he could and he would, and he did. What were Horace's actual words?	399
17	*"If you're not tired now, you will tomorrow." Why is this not correct?	399
18	*"He finished the job in two hours, but I don't know how he managed to do." Either take a word out, or put one in, to make this acceptable.	400
19	"Mary's having her hair cut and wants me to do it." Does she want me to cut my hair, or hers?	400

20	"What . . . . . . Hannibal do?" ". . . . . . he did was . . ." Fill the gaps meaningfully.	400
21	"I suppose so." What do I suppose?	401
22	What is the equivalent of *so* in another language that you know?	401
23	"Can't I say 'I'm sure so.'?" "I'm afraid . . . ." Complete the response.	401
24	Express your doubts about Thomas's claim that he speaks ten languages.	401
25	FLO: Does Frank know Tokyo? JOE: I don't know. Does Joe know Tokyo?	401
26	*"We may come, but I'm still not sure whether." What have we omitted to do?	402
27	ROSE: Why didn't he do it? MARY: Because I told him	403
28	"Go if you want to go, but someone ought to go with you. Shall I ask Gordon to go with you?" Which four words ought to go too?	403
29	"Take an umbrella. If you forget it, you'll regret it." Does *it* mean the same in both cases?	404, 391
30	DOCTOR: Herbert has broken his leg in five places. MOTHER: *How do you know it? Shall we amputate it, or replace it?	404
31	"Sir Humphrey said he would be delighted to give a speech at the meeting. This was very encouraging to the organisers." What was very encouraging?	404
32	Are you able, in some other language you know, to shorten sentences by omitting what would otherwise be repeated?	405

33	"He ran well. He did not run fast enough to win the race." What is the quickest way to coordinate these sentences?	406
34	"Mark was hungry and ate six bananas." *"Mark was so hungry that ate six bananas." What is wrong with the second sentence?	406
35	"Working eighteen hours a day, Arnold had no time for golf." Why didn't Arnold have any time for golf?	407
36	"A form which is often used in writing is the non-finite clause." Use it then!	407
37	"Though staggering with exhaustion, . . ." Complete the sentence.	408
38	*"Because not feeling well, Jim fell out of the race." Drop a word out to put the sentence right.	409
39	"They've decided to come since you invited them." Is this ambiguous?	409
40	"The school has improved since your taking over as headmaster." When or why?	409

UNIT FOURTEEN

Attracting attention

CGE REFERENCE: MEANINGS IN CONNECTED DISCOURSE: 411–423

Presenting and focusing information

Here again intonation is relevant to many of the questions, and your answers will often need to be marked for stress and intonation. Refer if you wish to **Part Two** of your CGE.

1	In written English, how many pieces of information are there in the following sentence: "Penelope, who dyed her h<u>ǎ</u>ir green, surprised her fr<u>iè</u>nds."	411
2	"I like ch<u>èe</u>se | and tom<u>à</u>toes." "I like cheese and tom<u>à</u>toes." What's the difference?	411
3	"There's a man over there with a g<u>ù</u>n." "There's a m<u>à</u>n over there. He's got a g<u>ù</u>n." How can you make the same distinction of meaning in spoken English without changing the words of the first sentence?	411
4	Give an example of a ONE-clause sentence containing ONE tone unit.	412
5	Give an example of a ONE-clause sentence containing TWO tone units.	412
6	Give an example of a TWO-clause sentence containing only ONE tone unit.	412

7 | "He asked her whether it was possible to have a cake with a cherry on it or not."
If *asked* and *possible* and *cherry* and *not* are all worth emphasising, how might we cut this sentence into more manageable mouthfuls? | 412

8 | "Classes will begin at ten thirty."
Where would you mark tone units? | 413

9 | "Yesterday morning at ten o'clock the rain came down in sheets."
Where would you mark tone units? | 413

10 | "Cream cakes which are fattening should be avoided."
Where would you mark tone units? | 413

11 | "And to sum up we should be careful about what we wear."
Where would you mark tone units? | 413

12 | "George stop pulling your sister's hair."
Where would you mark tone units? | 413

13 | "People who live in the country on the other hand are more relaxed."
Where would you mark tone units? | 413

14 | "Either say something or stop talking."
Where would you mark tone units? | 413

15 | "This is a grammar book."
Which is more relevant, the grammar or the book? | 414

16 | "She was wearing a lèather coat yésterday."
What assumptions can we make about today? | 415

17 | "Does Humphrey drink téa?"
What is the implication here? | 415

18 | "Henry VI had eight wives."
Correct this view of history. | 415

19 | "I know how they got ìnto the búilding . . ."
What might still be mystifying Dr Watson? | 416

20 | "The expert explained clearly hòw elephants work | for human béings, | but 'nobody told us . . . ."
How might the speaker continue this remark? | 416

21	"I said it was ìmpossible." Is this a word stress error?	416
22	Complete the following: "Pŏst-natal care | is even more important than . . . ."	416
23	"I know Sigmund dreamed a lŏt, | but what did he dream . . . . . .?" Provide the word and show the stress.	416
24	How is contrastive focus signalled in another language that you know?	416
25	"Alison was telling me about her new jòb." Which is the *given* information here?	417
26	"The train will now leave at twèlve forty-one." So what's new?	417
27	"Harry lòves cruckles | but Mary just can't stànd sweet things." What might a *cruckle* be?	417
28	"Hellŏ, | this is Sàm speaking." What's the one thing the listener needed to know?	418
29	"Hubert was driving hìs new car." What else might he have been doing?	418
30	"You can waste yŏur time | if you lìke, | but 'don't . . . ." Words and tone?	418
31	ALEXANDER: The phone's . . . . . . ing. GRAHAM: Answer it then. Fill the gap and mark the tone.	419
32	JACK: London stànds on the river Thàmes. JILL: What else could it do? What prompts Jill's sarcasm?	419
33	"Custard is Paula's favourite fòod." Has custard already been mentioned in this conversation?	420
34	"Cùstard is Paula's favourite fŏod." Has custard already been mentioned in this conversation? What about Paula?	420

35 | "Gwen started to feel better when she reached the h̲o̲spital." | 420
Which clause contains the main information?

36 | "Gwen started to feel be̲tter when she reached the hóspital." | 420
Where is the main information now?

37 | "Brian was hungry when he arrived." | 421
What intonation pattern would you use to make time the main item of information in this remark?

38 | "Brian was hungry when he arrived." | 421
Now focus on the state of Brian's stomach.

39 | "If you don't remove your d̲o̲nkey | I'll have to call the pol̆ice." | 422
What is wrong with the information structure here?

40 | "A large parrot on his shoulder screeching loud obscenities was what | 423
Long John Silver had."
Why is this odd? Try it the other way round.

UNIT FIFTEEN

Putting it all in order

CGE REFERENCE: MEANINGS IN CONNECTED DISCOURSE: 425–433

Order and emphasis: topic, fronting and inversion

Intonation remains important : see **Part Two** of your CGE, and mark your answers where necessary.

1	"Simon has ordered a new car." Why is this sentence typical of the way in which English orders information?	425
2	"The professor then switched to a completely new tòpic." Is *topic* the topic?	425
3	Where in the sentence, in another language that you know, does the most important part of the message usually come?	425
4	In what circumstances would someone say: "Rice pùdding | I órdered."	427
5	"An odd sèntence | thís is." Why?	427
6	"Mărmaduke | I lìke, | but . . ." Complete the sentence.	428
7	"Spĭders | . . . . . ., | but beĕtles | are all rìght." Insert a prepositional complement.	428

8	"...... she may be, but ...." Contrast two of her qualities.	428
9	"...... I'll come, but I can't ...." You can't promise, but you probably will. Complete this – and make sure the intonation is right.	428
10	"A good appetite I respect, but greed I abhor." Express these views in another language that you know, and compare the structure.	428
11	Which of the following is a complete utterance: "Some of the paintings Cŏnstable did" "Sŏme of the paintings | Cònstable did"	428
12	"However, this question we have already dealt with." What does *this* signal?	429
13	"I think we can all take this for granted." Turn this round to make it more < formal >.	429
14	"Up the steep path we struggled." Why should we say it in this way?	429
15	"All that you have said I agree with." How would you say this in another language?	429
16	"Up went the judge's flag." What is the purpose of this inversion?	430, 431
17	"...... in a million years ...... change his ways." Fill the blanks.	430
18	"In walked the Dean." Why is the Dean where he is?	431
19	"Down came the doomed aeroplane with flames pouring out of its engines." Comment on the sentence order.	431
20	*"There sunned himself Herbert, lying on the beach." "There lay Herbert, sunning himself on the beach." Why is one sentence acceptable, the other not?	431

21	*"His feet washed Norman carefully." Why would you reject this utterance?	431
22	"Carefully ⎫ "There ⎬ sat Norman washing his feet." ⎭ Which fits and which doesn't? Why?	431
23	"The starter's flag went down and the racing cars roared away." Make this commentary more dramatic.	431
24	*"And now the second car is also ready and away goes it." Why would you not hear this at the race-track?	431
25	"There are some ̱elephants." " 'There are some ̱elephants." Which sentence might make you run?	431
26	"Henry never spent a penny more than was necessary. Equally careful his brother Egbert was." How would you improve matters, and why?	431
27	"In all circumstances war is unjustified." Express your pacifism in a different way.	432
28	*"Only rarely he went out at night." Why is this unacceptable?	432
29	"Only in winter do they sleep" "Do they sleep only in winter" Punctuate these two sentences.	432
30	"Hardly ever . . ." Complete the sentence.	432
31	"Priscilla hardly realised what enormous problems her hasty words would cause." Rephrase, beginning with "Little . . .".	432
32	"Holmes didn't discover the truth until very much later." Rephrase, beginning with "Only . . .".	432
33	"Pictured here chatting to the Minister is Mr Percy Trifle, a ninety-four-year-old pastrycook from Rawtonstile." Where would you find something like this?	432

34	"So will I." What did the previous speaker say?	433
35	"So was mine." What did the previous speaker say?	433
36	"I've asked Jemima to come, and so has she." Who is *she*, and what has she done?	433
37	"I've asked Jemima to come, and so she has." Who is *she*, and what has she done?	433
38	"So have/am/was/did/will I." How would you say this in another language that you know?	433
39	How would you say "So they have." in another language that you know?	433
40	Complete the sentence: "So ridiculous . . ." Now rephrase your sentence.	433

UNIT SIXTEEN

Getting it all the right way round

CGE REFERENCE: MEANINGS IN CONNECTED DISCOURSE: 434–451

Order and emphasis: clefting, postponement and other positioning

1	"No, I want to marry Doris." How can we rearrange this sentence so that Doris is more strongly emphasised?	434
2	"Columbus discovered America in 1492." How can we rearrange this sentence to give more emphasis to the date?	434
3	"Eventually, it was Bob who was selected." Put it more briefly.	434
4	"We don't want empty words – . . . ." Voice your emphatic plea for action.	435
5	"I'd like a nice cup of tea." "A nice cup of tea is what I'd like." "What I'd like is a nice cup of tea." How would you make these distinctions in another language?	435
6	"I don't seek money – . . . ." Complete the contrast, using an it-type cleft sentence.	435

7	"Over there is where . . ." Complete the sentence.	436
8	"Stratford-upon-Avon is a great tourist attraction. It is . . . ." Complete in a way that explains the reason why Stratford is famous.	436(b)
9	"It was yesterday that I realised the truth." "When I realised the truth was only yesterday." Which is preferable?	436
10	"I hear there was a riot in Oxford Street." But you know that the incident occurred in Regent Street. React appropriately by stating the facts.	436
11	"We normally go to Lisbon in September." "It is in September that we normally go to Lisbon." Do these statements mean exactly the same thing?	436
12	*"Who pushed the victim to his death was Spike Muggins." How would you improve the style?	436
13	"What she is is a creative artist." Not very artistic! Would the *it*-type version be preferable?	437
14	*"It's wreck my new car that he's done." Repair the damage to the sentence!	437
15	*"What they're doing is to pretend to be innocent." But what is the writer guilty of? Can the sentence be reformed?	437
16	"What he'll do is discuss politics." "What he'll discuss is politics." Discuss the difference.	437
17	"Is John a carpenter?" How many different replies are possible if John is a plumber?	437
18	*"It's jumble the sentence that he's done." Can you unjumble it?	437
19	"That's . . . . . . I did it." "That's . . . . . . I like." "This is . . . . . . I was born." "That's . . . . . . she earns her money." Insert *wh*-words (but 4 h's, only 3 w's).	438

20	"This is why telephone boxes in the Lake District are painted with luminous paint." What does *this* refer to?	438
21	"It's unlikely that they'll come today." "That they'll come today is unlikely." Which of these is unlikely in conversation?	439
22	"It's impossible that Roger could have committed such a crime." Start the sentence with "That . . .". What effect does the inversion have?.	439
23	"It's 'likely I'll lose the elèction. It's a 'tough life being a politìcian." What's wrong with *being a politician*?	440
24	"You must find living with Margaret daunting." Rephrase this, using *it*.	441
25	Distinguish between: "The old man left it to his sons to decide." "The old man left it to his friends to divide."	441
26	"The moment when Andrew had to decide who his friends were came." Can you reduce the suspense and improve the sentence?	443
27	"The secret agent explained how he managed to keep silent in his own words." Relieve the ambiguity.	443
28	"I didn't get the builders in. I mended the roof myself." How would you say this in another language?	444
29	"Far more cures than used to be the case in the early part of this century are available today." Why is this sentence awkward? Remedy it.	445
30	"Not enough children to see Pinocchio's famous nose turned up." Is there a missing verb? Or what?	445
31	A: What causes rust? B: { Damp causes it. { It's caused by damp. Why is the second response more likely?	447

32	"He's wanted by the police." "The police want him." Why is the sentence better if *the police* are after *him*?	447
33	"That you were able to come after all delights me." Is there a more natural way of saying this?	447
34	"He was surprised by her remark." *"He was surprised by that she said that." Why is the second sentence unacceptable?	447
35	"He gave his possessions away." "He gave away his possessions." "He gave them away." *"He gave away them." Why is the last sentence not possible?	448
36	"The company has declared all tickets issued on or after March 17th, whether by themselves or by their agents, invalid." Is *invalid* in the wrong position?	448
37	"Randolph showed his stamp collection to the Senator's children." "Randolph showed the Senator's children his stamp collection." If these are responses, what question does each of them imply?	449
38	Does giving always imply receiving?	451
39	What do you have (or take) when you're tired? What about when you're thirsty?	451
40	In another language, would you visit the doctor or pay the doctor a visit?	451

UNIT SEVENTEEN

Making it sound right

CGE REFERENCE: VARIETIES OF ENGLISH

British and American
Written and spoken

Before tackling this unit and Unit Eighteen, read through **Part One** of your CGE which discusses and exemplifies many aspects of variation in English.

For questions dealing with variation between British and American English, look for the Ⓥ .

For questions dealing with variation between written and spoken English, look for the ⓥ .

Variations in formality are marked by ◈ .

1Ⓥ	"Your British friend hasn't any complaints." "Your American friend . . . . . . either!"	499
2Ⓥ	"The British Prime Minister Percival Forthright today resigned." Be briefer. (Be American.)	72, 490
3Ⓥ	"What's your son doing these days?" "He's at university." Oxford or Harvard?	73, 495
4Ⓥ	"One always gets one's just deserts." As an American, would you agree?	86

5☑	When the American / eɪt / a hamburger, what did his British companion do with his?	113, 616
6☑	"Our New York office didn't finish the assignment yet." "Never mind, the London office . . . . . . their part of the job either."	115
7☑	"I've gotten myself a son!" "Congratulations!" Whose population has just increased by one?	115, 604
8☑	Who might you be visiting if you are invited for a quarter of seven on December 12?	119, 668
9☑◇	"Used you to play hopscotch as a child?" Ask me again more <casually>.	120, 502
10☑	"I'm planning to visit Boston at the weekend." Which is more likely, Lincolnshire or Massachusetts?	143
11☑	Many Englishmen go to a football match every Saturday. Say what many Americans do on that day.	144
12☑	If I want to stay with my friends from Monday through Saturday, how many days will I spend with them, and where?	153
13☑	If you are in downtown Birmingham, are you in the Midlands or Alabama?	183
14☑	"British speakers say *while* or *whilst* whilst American speakers prefer . . . ." Who's telling you?	212, 830
15☑◇	"We're very educated, ain't we?" He ain't right, is he?	250, 500
16☑	If in America they say "Excuse me?", and in Britain they say "Sorry?", what do they say in other languages you know?	258
17☑	"The American committee has decided that the post remain open." Would a British committee announce its decision differently?	291
18☑	"Will you come?" "Well, I may, but then again I mayn't." Who may? Or who mayn't?	292, 501

19⃞ⓥ	You tell an American that the Statue of Liberty is being sold by auction. From his reply, you realise he doesn't believe you: "......!"	297
20⃞ⓥ	"Need we go to the party?" "No, we ...." Need we use *need*?	298
21⃞ⓥ	BARBARA: I gather you're annoyed with Marjorie. BRENDA: Yes, I'm mad at her. Who is talking to whom?	321
22ⓥ	"The quèstions | you knów | seem very èasy." Easy to say. But if you wrote this, what would you have to do?	323, 522
23⃞ⓥ	"I shan't tell you." Who won't?	339, 501
24ⓥ	"Right, so we're agreed the Company has the right to elect new board members without consulting the shareholders." State this regulation < formally > in your written Annual Report.	343(D)
25⃞ⓥ	RONALD: See you later. MARGARET: Cheerio. Who is saying goodbye to whom?	358
26⃞ⓥ	If a letter ends: ... Sincerely yours, Arthur Miller where was it probably posted?	360
27ⓥ ◈	If someone says "I'm extremely sorry", could it be because they have just sneezed while you were speaking?	361
28⃞ⓥ	"Excuse me. Is anyone serving here?" Say it differently in the States.	365
29ⓥ	MAURICE: We found a puppy while we were on holiday last year. Well, we adopted it and it's a member of the family. Now let me tell you something else about the holiday .... DORIS: Now that's interesting, because when we were visiting Canada my son fell off a cliff. What is odd in what each speaker says?	368

30 Ⓥ | "To begin with, come to dinner. Secondly, bring your wife." | 370
Odd?

31 Ⓥ ◇ | "I shall be leaving London shortly, viz. next Monday morning." | 373
Would you say that?

32 Ⓥ | Rewritten, this sentence could sound less formal. | 388
So rewrite it.

33 Ⓥ | "Will you answer the question?" | 399
"I have done."
Who has?

34 Ⓥ | "I'm too t̀ired | I can't go ̀on" | 411
"I'm so t̀ired | I can't go ̀on"
If you wrote these two sentences down, what punctuation would you need?

35 Ⓥ | "An author is someone who writes. | 412
An author is someone who writes books.
An author is someone who sweats blood to write books.
An author is someone who sweats blood to write books which nobody buys."
Break up these four sentences into ten tone units in all.

36 Ⓥ | "The lecturer told the students they would all pass provided they worked hard and paid attention in class." | 422
How would you rewrite this with maximum emphasis?

37 Ⓥ ◇ | "You're wearing a nice hat." | 427
< Informally > emphasise this remark.

38 Ⓥ | "Most of these claims the government has been prevaricating over for years." | 429
Are you more likely to hear this sentence or to read it?

39 ◇ Ⓥ | "Silence in court. Here comes the judge!" | 431
Pass sentence on these sentences.

40 Ⓥ | "It is in writing rather than speech that . . . . . . is particularly useful." | 434
Fill the gap.

UNIT EIGHTEEN

Putting on the style

CGE REFERENCE: VARIETIES OF ENGLISH

Formal and informal
Polite and familiar

For this unit as for Unit Seventeen, before working through the questions make sure that you have studied **Part One** of your CGE. The symbols will help to show the type of variation involved.

For questions dealing with variation between written and spoken English, look for the ⓥ .

Variations in formality are marked by ◈ .

1ⓥ	"Lots of problems were shared by most of the students." Rewrite this as in an official report.	58, 60
2◈	"We shall return to this point in our conclusion." Whose conclusion?	85
3◈	"You're lucky to get a job straight out of university these days." Am I necessarily talking to an ex-student?	86
4◈	"It is obvious that the trade negotiations will not reach a satisfactory conclusion for ages." What else is obvious?	156
5ⓥ◈	"Many flights have been cancelled on account of adverse weather conditions." Report this news to a friend over the phone.	199

6 ◇ | "Why are you carrying an umbrella?" | 203
"...... the sun gets too hot!" the Englishman replied sarcastically.

7 ◇ | This sentence is written in a formal style and consequently is | 202,
somewhat lengthy. | 204
This sentence is less formal, ... it is briefer.

8 ◇ | "In case of difficulty, just give me a ring." | 209
Can you improve on this casual offer?

9 ◇ | "Jack Sprat could eat no fat, | 212
His wife could eat no lean, . . ."
Write this as a more < formal > report by a dietician.

10 ◇ | "We may not reach the moon, but it'll have been a brave attempt | 216
. . . ."
Complete the statement appropriately.

11 ◇ | "How far do we see eye to eye?" < informal > | 217
"To . . . . . . do you feel that our opinions coincide?"< formal >

12 ◇ | "Do you have something slightly cheaper?" | 219
"Yes, but it's a great deal less reliable."
Express this dialogue in language which is a little less < formal >.

13 ◇ | "The country needs doctors. It needs trained nurses too." | 238
State these manpower requirements less< informally> in one sentence.

14 ◇ | "How old are you?" | 253
"Don't be impertinent, young man!"
How might you enquire more discreetly about the lady's age?

15 ◇ | "I'm going on holiday next week." | 255
"Who with?"
"Mind your own business!"
If you want to find out, try being more< polite >.

16 ◇ | "I came by bus today." | 257
"You did what?"
"There's no need to sound so surprised."
So don't be.

17 ◇ | "I beg your pardon?" "What?" | 258
How would you say these in another language?

18◈ Should you rephrase this, it would sound more informal and less   286
tentative.

19◈ "Looks like rain tomorrow."   305
Who says so, your neighbour or the weather forecaster?

20◈ "Doctor, my wife's condition gives me cause for concern."   333
Be more natural.

21◈ In at least four different ways, find out whether you may refer to your   340
books in the examination.

22◈ You have to be home by eleven, and it's nearly that now. What would   341
you say to your friends before leaving?

23◈ You need some sugar for your tea.   349
Ask for it in as many ways as you can, but make sure you are very
< familiar > and very < polite > at least once.

24◈ "Have lunch with me tomorrow."   351
"No."
Translate this into more < formal > and < polite > English.

25◈   354

SECURITY AREA
Please don't enter
without a pass

Be strict and provide for firmer security.

26◈◉ "Once we've got your manuscript, we can let you have the printed   355
copy in six months."
Write this as a < formal > offer.

27◈ ANN: Hi, John.   358
JOHN: Hi, Ann.
ANN: This is Professor Nollidge.
JOHN: Hello.
Make this more < formal >.

28◈ "Bye bye, Madam."   358
"Cheerio, Fortescue, and ta for the lift home."
Would you hire this scriptwriter?

29 ⟨v⟩ | Dear Miss Brown,
           Meet me off the 12 o'clock train on Tuesday.
                Yours sincerely,
                  Jonathan.
Write two better versions of this letter. | 360

30 ⟨v⟩ | How would you turn down the offer of the Nobel Prize for Literature? | 361

31 ⟨v⟩ | "Say hello to Mort for me!"
Are you going to walk up to Mort and say "Hello" next time you see him? | 362

32 ⟨v⟩ | What forms of address are used in another language you know? | 365

33 ⟨v⟩ ⟨v⟩ | "Here's the book you wanted me to get you. Incidentally, you owe me another pound."
Which word could you improve on? | 369

34 ⟨v⟩ ⟨v⟩ | "I do not intend to participate in your seminar. What's more, I shall instruct my colleagues also to withdraw."
Which expression could you improve on? | 371

35 ⟨v⟩ ⟨v⟩ | "Tomato soup, please."
"Sorry, no tomato. We do, nevertheless, have mushroom."
A likely situation, but unlikely language. Make it consistent. | 376

36 ⟨v⟩ | "I went to bed early. Moreover, I slept like a log."
Improve on this. | 377

37 ⟨v⟩ | "Clear this mess up . . . . . . I'll tell your Dad."
Complete this maternal thought. | 382

38 ⟨v⟩ | "Who wants to wash up?"
< Informally > decline this optimistic invitation. | 398

39 ⟨v⟩ ⟨v⟩ | "Being a very formal sort of person, Worthington used to fill his letters with sentences of this kind."
Of what kind? | 407

40 ⟨v⟩ ⟨v⟩ | So . . . . . . is where *Talking About Grammar* must come to an end.
They do say . . . . . .'s what happens to all good things! | 438

KEY TO THE QUESTIONS

Not every question has a 'correct' answer. Where the key cannot help you any more than the paragraph referred to in CGE, you will find simply a dash: —.

Many questions are open to a wide range of answers, incorporating your own ideas. The key can only offer an example of a good response. In these cases the key is marked 'e.g.'

Possible alternative answers are shown like this: xxx / yyy;

or like this: $\begin{cases} \text{xxx} \\ \text{yyy} \end{cases}$

Remember that it is the CGE paragraph, rather than the key, that will give you full understanding of the point of a question. Information available in your CGE is not repeated in the key.

UNIT ONE

1 Either! The government as a unit, or members of the government. (*Can* can have a singular or a plural subject.)

2 *Of* is optional in "(a) half of a loaf" but obligatory in "a quarter of a loaf" and in all other fractions.

3 Sheets/pieces of paper; bars of gold (or chocolate); coils of rope; planks of wood. But not *planks of metal or *bars of rubber.

4 (a) Right.
  (b) Wrong: *fathom* measures depth of water.

(c) Wrong: *quart* measures liquid.
(d) Right.
(e) Right: nails can be weighed.
(f) Right: paint is liquid (though you are likely to buy it by the *litre* nowadays).

5 Three:
This type of weapon is dangerous.
These types of weapon are dangerous.
These type of weapons are dangerous.< informal >
But we wouldn't normally say *"This type of weapons", and anything beginning *"This types of . . ." is clearly unacceptable.

6 Where two masses of water meet, e.g. two rivers.

7   —

8   No: *all* of them were absent.

9   No. "I have *a few* friends" would be more optimistic.

10   A lot of thought – and lots of time too!

11   No, two: ten pounds or one pound.

12   Two candidates. Three or more parties.

13   "Anything" (i.e. any digestible substance, however unappetising).

14   —

15   Five examples are needed: back-pointing, forward-pointing, unique, institutional, generic.

16   The first is an incorrect generic description: bananas are normally yellow. The second may be a good specific description (for example, if these particular bananas are over-ripe).

17   The morphology of the English verb.

18   "The rich . . . the poor . . .!" The generic use of the adjective.

19   "*a* London of austerity": London has many faces, at this time austere.
"*the* London of the 60s": London at one specific time.

20   One lady, but who knows which? John is unquestionably dead.

21   "him". The baby's sex is known and we are about to hear a boy's name.

22   A problem. While we cannot assume that all feminists are female, there is no one pronoun which includes both *he* and *she* to cover all persons regardless of sex. (S/he is an unpronounceable <formal> written expedient.)

23   Mrs Brown's. The doctor is being condescending.

24   Non-smokers say so. So do the health authorities.

25   *That* is what you just said; *this* is what I'm going to tell you now.

26   The newscaster is about to present it.

27   *This* is used<familiarly>here to introduce a topic – not, fortunately, to refer to an actual object!

28   No: people are afraid of witches – live in fear of them.

29   Wood, perhaps: but it *contains* salad.

30   "John": the 'have' relation.

31   His father hates him: the SUBJECT-VERB relation. But it could also be that he hates his father: the VERB-OBJECT relation.

32   Yes, the company decided: SUBJECT-VERB relation.
No, someone founded the company: VERB-OBJECT relation.

33   Not unless the girl tells a story about a girl: the ORIGIN relation.

34   **e.g.** SUBJECT-VERB relation: "Alexander Graham Bell's invention of the telephone . . ."

35   **e.g.** "The birthday of the oldest person in Egypt . . ."

36   *With* = opposition when used in conjunction with the word *war*. So you are against me.

37   "Books are made of paper" but "Paper is made from wood".

38   Yes: the restrictive relative clause implies that not all elephants weigh over a ton. (But a couple of commas would make a big difference.)

39   We don't know; perhaps none of them.

40   Only you can decide: "the last difficult question" (restrictive) would suggest that you found other questions difficult too!

UNIT TWO

1   Make sure you mention a STATE, a SINGLE EVENT and a SET OF REPEATED EVENTS.

2   In Humpty's case, a habit rather than a state: and he is clearly capable of changing his habits.

3   It would be difficult to find a better one.

4   It may not be sensible, but it is a habit.

5   No, because the progressive aspect indicates limited duration.

6   Don't count on a temporary habit.

7   Again and again: and it's a nuisance.

8   We really don't know, but they are not necessarily arguing throughout: the important thing is that they happen to be doing so every time I repeat my visit.

9   "Could I give you a hand?"

10   His wife, not him.

11   Richard Rodney Bennett. The activity of composing is not finished.

12   Mozart, who is dead, composed great works during his lifetime.

Pele, who is alive, no longer plays football.

13   Well, not the President in office at the moment.

14   "has been" (state leading up to the present time).

15   To be precise, at an indefinite time in an indefinite place!

16   No: a habitual event but not (we trust) a continuous one!

17   Your appetite. (Keep it up and you may lose some weight too!)

18   No: within a period of limited duration leading up to the present.

19   It puts us into a definite time in the past, and makes us cast our minds further back still.

20   You might have (if you haven't heard the result yet, or have heard, but failed).
     Alternatively, you didn't: you regret not having taken it.

21   ". . . I haven't received/had a reply."

22   Try *since*.

23   Acceptable in < spoken > English.

24   "When . . ." refers to past habit. "If . . ." expresses a wish.

25   "falls" for HISTORIC PRESENT narrative; "fell" for SIMPLE PAST narrative. Note that *hit* may be simple present or simple past.

26   Most unlikely: SIMPLE PRESENT tense with verbs of communication.

27   Perhaps this morning: a single past event.

28   Perhaps during my childhood: a past habit.

29   STATE UP TO PAST TIME:
      ⎰ "... up to the time we left."
      ⎱ "... by tea-time."
        "... before me – I was
        surprised!"

30   —

31–   Check your examples against the
40   **chart** in paragraph 139 to see
      whether they are correct. Check
      them against your **conscience** to
      know whether they are true.

UNIT THREE

1   Not necessarily; perhaps he
      stayed, after all.

2   "The audience was just leaving
      ..." (or 'were': see 1.1) avoids
      the impression of cause and
      effect which the simple past
      gives.

3   **e.g.** "... I was reading a book."
      "... I went to bed."

4   **e.g.** "... fears/believes things are
      getting worse."

5   "Telephone rings."

6   Verbs of perceiving generally
      don't take progressive aspect.

7   They rarely take progressive
      aspect, remember?

8   He must currently be in
      London.

9   Whenever you think about them
      (including now).

10   Let's hope it's just a passing
      internal sensation.

11   Nothing at all (apart from either
      Penny's constitution or Jenny's
      eyesight).

12   "We've been hearing a lot about
      oil exploration recently.": *hear*
      as a mental activity.

"We hear a lot about oil
exploration from time to time.":
hear as a state verb.

13   "We are hoping so."

14   **e.g.** "The 2.40 train from
      Duncton will arrive at platform
      seven."

15   Remember:
      if + simple present ... *will* ...
      or:
      ... *will* ... *if* + simple present

16   "I'll go." / "I'll get it." / "I'll see
      who it is."

17   You don't know for sure; but you
      do know his intentions.

18   **e.g.** "... is going to boil over."

19   No, but at this minute we're
      expecting to go out later.

20   "flies", "passes", or just "is".

21   Probably tomorrow: present
      tense referring to future. (But
      "I hope it's not too hot" could
      refer to the present cup of tea!)

22   Because we are referring to the
      timetable according to which the
      exams are scheduled.

23   Because the speaker has already
      decided to call his lawyers.

24   <Politely>, to soften our
      intention.

25   Your holiday is not an official
      arrangement for the future, but
      the Prime Minister's visit is. So
      switch the verb forms.

26   **e.g.** "... they gave themselves
      up."

27   Fulfilled future in the past – the
      story can go on to give the
      reasons for his regret.

28   You'll have tackled another
      twelve problems!

29   Temporary habit.

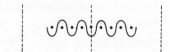

30   —

31   Temporary state to present time.

32   No.

33   Habitual present.

34   —

35   Future event arising from present action. Try "are to" (135) and "will be" (129).

36   Past in future time.

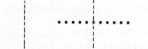

37   Yes.

38   Past before past event.

39   Single present event.

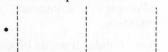

40   Habit up to present time (and let's hope the growth continues!).

UNIT FOUR

1   Did you get an adverb, a prepositional phrase, a noun phrase, a noun phrase with *ago* (etc), and an adverbial clause?

2   "will be/is Tuesday."
"is the day after tomorrow."

3   "At . . ."

4   "On . . ."

5   "In . . ."

6   *During, over, throughout;* but NOT *between, on* or *at.*

7   { "From . . . to . . ."
"Between . . . and . . ."

8–   Use time references from
10   paragraphs 141, 142, 143.

11   "by night"

12   —

13   "Send the telex on Sunday."
"The office is closed (on) Sundays."

14   "I last saw John the week before last."
or:
"I last saw John a week last Thursday."

15   e.g. "Earn before you spend." / "Listen before you talk." / "Don't complain before you know the facts."

16   e.g. "By March." / "By the end of term." / "By next Friday!"

17   By 8 o'clock.

18   e.g. "I've already handed it in."
"I haven't finished yet."

19   e.g. ". . . in six and a half hours."
But how good is your car?

20   —

21 **e.g** "In five days." / "Five days from now." / "In five days' time."

22 Yes.

23 "ago" . . . "from now"

24 No: "at this moment" . . . "a short time ago"

25 Since he was rude.

26 **e.g.** "when" / "once" / "as soon as"

27 "When did you enter the country?"
"*On March the fourth.*"
"I see, and how long did you stay in Cairo?"
"*For three weeks.*"
"And when did you visit Luxor?"
"*Over the weekend.*"
"So how long have you been staying in Egypt?"
"*Since the fourth of March.*"
"And when does your plane leave?"
"*While we are arguing about my visa, I reckon!*"

28 **e.g.** "He isn't able to sleep all night." / "He can't sleep for long." / "He stays awake the whole time."

29 Not Sebastian. The runner who pipped him at the post.

30 **e.g.** Don't look at the paper *before* you are told to do so. Remain silent *while* the examination is in progress. You must not leave *until* the bell rings.

31 Be careful with STATE and EVENT.

32 <u>until</u>

33 "Recently" = lately. "For ages" = for a long time.

34 —

35 Four.

36 **e.g.** "Yes, I have dined at the Palace on many occasions."

37 Every year some students are bound to be worried (but not necessarily all of them, and clearly not the same students).

38 —

39 —

40 —

UNIT FIVE

Many of the problems set in this unit leave you a very free choice of expression, so we can't predict your answer! Wherever you see the word CHECK in the key, look back carefully at the relevant paragraph in *A Communicative Grammar of English* and study the examples given.

1 —

2–3 CHECK

4 No, but you can see right through it.

5 Yes: "We entered the park." "We were inside the park, walking round it."

6 CHECK

7 Three: explore the map.

8 In the multi-storey car park; and in the market place *except on Fridays*.

9 CHECK: and use your imagination.

10 Long-distance if it stops *at* Duncton on the way *to* another town. The local bus stops at various points *in* Duncton.

11   Christopher Columbus sailed from Europe to the New World. Marco Polo travelled from Europe to China.

12   In Duncton; at the Town Hall; in the High Street.

13   **e.g.** "He shouted *at* me."

14   CHECK

15   CHECK

16   Under or beneath a church.

17   He has to learn that the red light is *above* the orange light, while the green light is *below* the orange light.

18   CHECK

19   "The river flows *beneath/under* the bridge." "There's deep water *under(-neath)* the bridge." (But *below* the bridge would imply *downstream from*, = *towards the sea*.)

20   CHECK

21   A prepositional adverb, not a preposition of position (though you could say "in the front of the car"). Contrast it with "in the back" (you can*not* say *"in back').

22   "above" . . . "love"

23   "amid" < formal >

24   CHECK

25   CHECK

26   CHECK

27   CHECK

28   CHECK (and look out for one-way streets)

29   However far you walk *up* it, it's probably on the level.

30   CHECK

31   Just walk across the road.

32   On Fridays.

33   A book or two, since you would be in the library.

34   There will be stalls on Fridays, and cars on other days.

35   Past repairing and beyond repair.

36   Under his command, and above average (perhaps even above reproach).

37   Get off the bus!

38   CHECK

39   "through" indicates the length of the tunnel; "under" indicates its depth beneath the summit of the mountain.

40   —

UNIT SIX

1   **e.g.** "slowly" (MANNER) / "by manual labour" (MEANS) / "with ramps and sledges" (INSTRUMENT).

2   The same way as you (do) . . . or the way you like.

3   "in a workmanlike manner"

4   It's difficult. Demonstration is much easier: you can simply say "like this" and do it!

5   "like a chimney"

6   **e.g.** ". . . as if I were inferior." / ". . . as if I were a child."

7   If you answer it *without* referring to the paragraph, you may miss an important use of *by*.

8   With your knife (as INSTRUMENT): and obviously with pleasure too!

9   "By . . . (phone, for example)."

10   **e.g.** "The famous actor discovered the identity of the secret agent."

11   **e.g.** "The famous actor was therefore kidnapped by the secret agent."

12   **e.g.** "Because they want to." / "Out of bravado." / "From a sense of adventure." (But the classic answer is: "Because they're there.")

13   ". . . on account of the weather." / ". . . because the weather was bad." . . . ". . . because of / on account of his injury."

14   Through his own efforts (thus often relieving God of a great responsibility).

15   The heat will cause the glass to break.

16   Let us hope that the effect of universal education is to avert universal catastrophe.

17   Chickens lay eggs, so the chickens come first. Chickens hatch from eggs, so the eggs come first.

18   It's the home of 'Kentucky Fried Chicken', *so* they've probably all been eaten!

19   **e.g.** "So as to get to the other side."; or "In order to . . ."; or just "To . . .".

20   **e.g.** "He killed her *out of* jealousy." (The prosecution.) "He put her out of her misery *from* a sense of pity." (The defence.)

21   **e.g.** "Since I've put on a lot of weight . . ."

22   **e.g.** "I overdid it, and consequently . . ."

23   **e.g.** "Microcomputers, having become less expensive, are in great demand."

24   **e.g.** Marie Curie is famous for discovering radium. Walt Disney is famous for his animated cartoons.

25   "We are thus/accordingly/hence obliged to cancel your membership."

26   ". . . if he needs it." (209 would give an alternative.)

27   Probably: ". . . I'd fail it." He clearly doesn't intend to try yet.

28   **e.g.** "on condition that" / "provided (that)" / "so long as": the last would be best if you were talking less < formally >.

29   Probably "IN CASE OF FIRE"

30   You won't know why unless you do!

31   "But for . . ."

32   **e.g.** "If you ever visit London, you must come and stay with me."

33   —

34   **e.g.** "The car was a write-off, but I escaped without a scratch." "Although I was badly shaken, I wasn't hurt."

35   Commonly: "Unaccustomed as I am to public speaking, . . ."

36   Try "Despite . . ."; and ". . . yet".

37   **e.g.** "He didn't even finish it!" "He didn't even take it!"

38   **e.g.** "even though he . . ."

39   "Whether we like it or not!"

40   "Wherever she goes."

UNIT SEVEN

1   **e.g.** "Quite a bit." / "Very much!"

2   **e.g.** "Enormously." / "Immensely."

3   Quite old by a young man's standards – and very young compared with the old!

4   *Quite* intensifies the meaning only slightly; *absolutely* indicates extreme intent; and *half-witted* is not a limit word (cf. *insane*).
So the speaker is more than a little careless – if not utterly slovenly!

5   **e.g.** "I'd be very surprised."

6   **e.g.** "Prices have gone up quite a lot."

7   —

8   **e.g.** "Completely absurd." / "Almost impossible." / "Quite marvellous."

9   No, just rather unexpected.

10 I'll send you my *best* wishes – no, on second thoughts, my *very best* wishes.

11 Include a premodifier, a mid-position and an end-position adverbial.

12 No. Wait until it's a little cooler.

13 **e.g.** "Very angry indeed." or "Absolutely infuriated."

14 —

15 Ssssh! Not one you can't hear at all, but one you can scarcely hear.

16 How about "badly" . . . "hard" . . . "thoroughly"?

17 **e.g.** As a student, you're outstanding. You speak English well for a student. And you're very good at grammar!

18 Model answers are difficult in that we don't know your views.

19 Jill is less careful than Jack.
Jill is not as careful as Jack (is).

20 —

21 We hope this one is cheaper and better.

22 **e.g.** "Aluminium is less malleable than lead, while lead is more malleable than gold."
"Aluminium is the cheapest metal, lead is costlier, gold is the most expensive."
"Half a pound of iron is as light (the same weight) as eight ounces of feathers."

23 We're sure you find them all superlative. But be precise.

24 It's getting higher and higher. And it's getting more and more difficult to make ends meet!

25 **e.g.** "It's too cold/not fertile enough . . ."

26 **e.g.** "Is the water cool enough yet?"

27 —

28 ". . . there's so little space that . . ."

29 —

30 "Less of a victory than a defeat." or "More (of) a defeat than a victory."

31 However you finish it, the end starts with *the*.

32 **e.g.** "As well as English, I study soil science."

"In addition, I study
comparative literature."

33   **e.g.** "Write with his left
hand as well as his right hand/
and his right hand too."

34   **e.g.** Wood floats on water, and so
does oil.
Wood doesn't sink. Neither
does oil.

35   "but for / except for / apart from
Hector."

36   **e.g.** " – even old shoes." /
" – even grammar books!"

37   Only members can play. The
courts are open only from 9.00 to
7.00. They are only open during
the week. Even then you must
book in advance.

38   "Only the best"

39   She *also* studies French (as well
as my son).
She also studies *French* (as well
as Italian).

40   Presumably you would rather be
fully *considered* (thought about)
than come to the speaker's mind
as a passing fancy (thought of).

UNIT EIGHT

1   People usually know who they
are – and they don't normally ask
questions which seek
information they already have
(unless, perhaps, they are
teachers!).

2   Yes, he is. (Not: Yes, he is
wasting his breath!)

3   A *yes* or *no* is called for; and the
answer is not the information
Angus needs.

4   No. The intonation has not fallen
yet. Nor has *or* appeared.

5   The first speaker is more patient.

6   Yes. *Some* expects a more
positive answer.

7   *Some* is more <polite>, and less
reluctant.

8   That the other person hasn't.

9   She probably isn't hungry. So
she'll say "No."

10   Routine confirmation is all that is
needed. (When is a question not
a question?)

11   So you've arrived at the answer,
have you?

12   At bed-time, presumably.

13   **e.g.** "By post, tomorrow, in
London." Informative and brief
(only five!).

14   Yes. The first is more <polite>:
the station is in the same place,
but we are more likely to find it.

15   When I answer the door or the
phone.

16   "Where?" . . . "Why?" Ted is
keeping it short.

17   **e.g.** "Twenty past séven?"
(disbelieving and brief).
"Whát time did you say?"
(request for repetition).
"Twenty past whát?"
(question word later in
sentence, <familiar> and
brief).
And more ways than this.

18   Sorry I didn't hear you the first
time.

19   Something with which I absolutely agree.

20   Obviously, the object which the label is stuck on.

21   "You", and "I".

22   Because *he* is only a pronoun. (Compare ". . . suggested Tom.")

23   "Let's decide here and now."

24   The first *should* does not express obligation, the second does.

25   George is expressing a general truth.

26   Vocal effect and indirect speech don't go together. Try *exclaimed*.

27   "Do you like cheese?"

28   Whether it was John's or Mary's.

29   —

30   In the second case.

31   Jessica ate something – in fact, a good deal.

32   Yes. It is quite common for them to do so.

33   When someone has suggested he hasn't.

34   That you did.

35   ERNEST: I agree. (or: No, they shouldn't.)

36   No, it isn't. But this is!

37   Because Aunt is a <tactful> person.

38   **e.g.** "Are you súre? | I had the impression Wàshington was." Not " 'No, it ìsn't."

39   "but . . ."

40   "I am not (may not be) rich, but I am healthy."

UNIT NINE

1   It's rather impolite.

2   Agreement and regret.

3   "No." (disagreement) "Yes." (enthusiastic agreement)

4   "Completely right." (enthusiastic agreement) "Fairly good." (judgment)

5   The first, yes. The second <tactfully> implies disagreement.

6   **e.g.** ". . . there are many similarities."

7   **e.g.** ". . . and say . . ."

8   No. Falsehood is assumed.

9   Yes. Truth is assumed.

10   Hypothesis. Present or future, but not past (*had*, not *had had*).

11   He hasn't got a watch.

12   No, they didn't: hypothetical past. Perhaps they will: hypothetical future.

13   I am not you.

14   **e.g.** "If more jobs were to be threatened, we should have to take industrial action." (B) or: "If more jobs should be threatened, we would have to take industrial action." (C)

15   Lawyer – or a very <literary> friend!

16   No. It may be a hypothetical conditional.

17 Yes, because contraction is not allowed in a negative hypothetical conditional.

18 Maybe: NEUTRALITY.

19 *That* is for FACT. *Whether* is for NEUTRALITY.

20 In the first sentence, whether she told you; in the second, whether she is married.

21 I might visit Paris. If so, I ought to climb the Eiffel Tower.

22 (1) FACTUAL *that* (followed by PUTATIVE *should*),
    (2) demonstrative *that*,
    (3) the word *that*.

23 No, the chairman is only expressing an intention.

24 No, not without a comma!

25 **e.g.** a. It may rain.
         b. It is possible that it will rain.
         c. Perhaps it will rain.

26 Theoretical possibility versus factual possibility.

27 Suicide is always fatal, not only sometimes: 'attempted suicide', of course, is not.

28 Past time or hypothetical *could*.

29 **e.g.** "You could be wrong."

30 No. The first expresses past ability and achievement: *were able to* cannot be replaced by *could*.
    The second is hypothetical.

31 The first expresses logical necessity, the second obligation.

32 **e.g.** "It doesn't have to." / "Not necessarily." / "It needn't." / "Yes, it should."

33 The first means "It was necessary for George to stop." The second means "It is (almost) certain that George stopped."

34 Habitually, or characteristically, any time.

35 Now. PREDICTION about the (as yet unconfirmed) present.

36 No. He thinks it's probable.

37 I am not certain whether he is honest.

38 "I think Patience was ill." (belief)
    "I observed Patience and judged that she was ill." (opinion)

39 **e.g.** "I don't think so."

40 —

UNIT TEN

1 "Good!"
   "Well!"

2 —

3 "?" (This is a question.)
   "!" (This is an interjection.)

4 "So much, so loud". Emphatic.

5 A matter of degree: the judgment is yours.

6 The first is more emphatic (perhaps refuting a denial).

7 Jacques', of course.

8 *Awful* means *very bad*, yet *awfully nice* means *extremely nice*.

9 **e.g.** "I really mean it."

10 An intensified exclamation. A philosophical question of global proportions!

11 *Wherever* has intensified emotive force.

12 **e.g.** "a penny" / "a cent" / "a thing".

13 It intensifies the impossibility. It indicates uncertainty.

14 "Was he angry!"

15 Do you really expect an answer to this question?

16 No.

17 It's a rhetorical question! (The rest of the quotation – indeed the rest of the play – is relevant to the possible answer.)

18 No. His friends caused his anger.

19 **e.g.** "I was pleased to see you at our party."
    "I was delighted that I could come."

20 *Cheerfully*. It can't modify a sentence.

21 Minimal. The 'act of acting' and the 'idea of acting' are barely distinguishable for many speakers.

22 No: *enjoy* only takes -ing clauses.

23 "We prefer buses to trains."

24 **e.g.** "I hope (that) we will meet at midnight."
    or: "I hope to meet you at midnight."

25 I anticipate that it will be good.

26 No, I didn't. And I regret it now.

27 **e.g.** "What an excellent book!"

28 She wouldn't think much of either, in terms of frequency or degree!

29 No, not really. It's <tactful> but forceful disapproval.

30 —

31 "How odd!" (Not the shoes but the fact.)

32 It means "I will (am willing to) marry." (part of the wedding ceremony).

33 *Would* (if he saw one): an exaggeration of course, so not really likely.

34 —

35 Yes. But it's less <tentative> and <tactful> .

36 I see something I really want, but I can't afford it.
    I am rejecting a suggestion which I consider indulgent or expensive.

37 **e.g.** "Would you care to dance?" or "Shall we dance?"

38 "intends"
    "carries the same meaning as"

39 "am going" (intention plus prediction)

40 Habitually and insistently. "He 'will keep tàlking."

UNIT ELEVEN

1 Yes. Could be a question of his ability or a request for permission.

2 Now, since I <tactfully> wish to enquire; in the future, when the occasion possibly arises.

3 'Request for permission' becomes 'request for action'.

4 **e.g.** Anxious parents to their party-going children.

5 'Sense of duty' versus 'imposed obligation': but the meanings are so close that the terms are generally interchangeable.

6 The latter.

7 You have to say "Yes, I have to." / "Yes, I must."

8 I very likely will.
I may or may not (we do not always go where duty calls!)

9 **e.g.** ". . . or you'll fail the exam." ". . . if you want to pass the exam."

10 Very different.
mustn't = be obliged not to (you might get electrocuted).
needn't = be not obliged to (you might find it difficult).

11 **e.g.** "You are to obey my orders."

12 **e.g.** "Up you get!" / "Away you go!"

13 **e.g.** "Quickly!" / "There!"

14 No. A severe command or regulation.

15 You, but "Don't you . . ." might sound impatient.

16 **e.g.** "Have a seat." / "Sit yourself down." / "Help yourself."

17 "Plèase make sure you arrive on tìme."
"Make sure you arrive on tĭme, please."
"Make sure you arrive on tĭme, | wòn't you."

18 —

19 **e.g.** "I wonder if you'd mind lending me . . ."
"I would be very grateful if you could loan me . . ."

20 **e.g.** "You'd better think it over carefully."
"I suggest you think it over carefully."

21 **e.g.** "You might try asking him."

22 *Let us* may be either a <formal> suggestion or a request for release.

23 "John suggested we have dinner together tonight." (Or "that night", depending on the time reference.)

24 It's difficult, having already said he's free – unless perhaps he claims he's on a diet!

25 She's just invited Antony to (come for) dinner.

26 Yes he did. Double negative = positive.

27 "If you eat one more of those, you'll be sick."

28 They all involve future time.

29 "Fred promised to come and see me – and Ned threatened to as well!"

30 Answering the phone and greeting the caller.

31 Yes. The speaker doesn't know whether he is coming or going.

32 Try following both with "How do you do? Pleased to meet you."

33 Not getting on anything. Just *getting on* with life in general or the job at hand.

34 Faith.

35 Not invariably, though Americans are likely to tell you "you're welcome".

36   Not forget.
Give my good wishes.

37   Yes. "Happy birthday!" (not everyone's idea of an achievement).

38   Yes, whether he said *please* or *thank you*.

39   A young couple talking to a priest.

40   (1) "Excuse me!" or "Waiter!"
(2) "Jack!" or "Jill!"
(3) "Mr. Hepworth!" or "Sir!" or "Miss/Mrs Maxwell!" or "Miss!" – or indeed, <informally>, "Jack!" or "Jill!"
(4) "My Lord!" ("M'lud!")
(5) "Sir!" or "Madam!"
(6) "Ladies and Gentlemen!"
(7) "Excuse me, Mr. Jones!" or "Excuse me, mate!"; depending on the locality, perhaps, and the degree of familiarity, certainly.

UNIT TWELVE

1   At the beginning, a change in your train of thought. At the end, present time (and perhaps a change of train!).

2   "Well, . . ."

3   Not normally. *By the way* changes the subject.

4   Yes.<Formal>linking signals in <informal> speech.

5   **e.g.** ". . . than a hot bath?" "A hot bath is good for you . . ."

6   Yes. Sequence of points or sequence of places?

7   **e.g.** "in any case"

8   —

9   **e.g.** "Besides, the set's broken."

10   No: it summarises our description of the various events which made up the holiday.

11   Certainly not. *In short* has nothing to do with height – though no doubt elegant Edna is just the right height too!

12   **e.g.** "Altogether"

13   "In a word, no."

14   **e.g.** "That is (to say)"

15   In <formal written> texts, to give a more precise description.

16   —

17   **e.g.** "rather" (or "at least")

18   **e.g.** "or rather" . . . "In other words" / "That is to say"

19   It shows they are simultaneous.

20   That he is about to say something which contrasts with what he has just said.

21   Either omit *although* or omit *but*.

22   Yes. A contrastive link between consistent ideas. ". . ., and he was terrified." would make more sense. (So would staying at home!)

23   In the first (subordinate) case, that Gertrude returned home. In the second (coordinate) case, nothing.

24   It specifies the sequence of events, rather than their simultaneity.

25   Try 4 – 2 – 1 – 3.

26   **e.g.** "Because he jumped too soon, he got killed."

27 Yes. But Mona's pills have unfortunate side-effects.

28 **e.g.** "If you eat an apple a day, you won't need a doctor."

29 Contrast with preceding idea. Condition + contrast with following idea.

30 *Not only* implies *but also* (additional fact).
    Not an only child implies brothers and sisters. (multiplication.)

31 "A woman who, as well as being a married woman, (also) has a paid job."

32 **e.g.** "We can go either to a concert or to the cinema."
    "We can go to a concert or else we can see a film."

33 Linking action to purpose. Linking cause to result.

34 "My husband is a comedian, *which* is no joke!"

35 The camel, unless you supply a comma, in which case the decision to ride all the way on a camel.

36 **e.g.** "When someone ill-treats children, he should be punished."
    "If anyone ill-treats children, he should be punished."

37 Very important. The difference between giving a reason ("..., I am often unemployed.") and making a statement ("... is not the steadiest of occupations.")

38 No. No.

39 He was. "..., because he was too embarrassed to speak."

40 Reason. Water-borne disease.

UNIT THIRTEEN

1 **e.g.** "Charlie was wearing a life-jacket and was saved."

2 Possibly Leo's, and perhaps Leo, given that boys will be boys. But we don't know.

3 **e.g.** "... I ... our ..."
    "... Fred ... your ..."

4 Yes.

5 "The Zygian public have ..." draws attention to the individuals within the group.
    "The Zagian public has ..." stresses the corporate decision.

6 "one" ... "some"

7 No. "White or brown?"

8 Because a count noun after *a* is represented by *one*: "... or a blue one?"

9 "that"

10 "those"

11 "... than that of the jungle."

12 Horace can play too, but he may not be as good as Peter.

13 Dick's. It's an <informal> question.

14 "do"

15 "I'll complain if you do/will."

16 "I can and I will."

17 *Be* cannot be omitted after *will*.

18 "... managed to." or "... managed to do so/it."

19 Hers.

20 "What did Hannibal do?"
    "What he did was cross the Alps."

21 That what you suppose/say/have said is right.

22   —

23   "not"

24   **e.g.** "I doubt if he does." / "I doubt it." / "I don't believe it."

25   We don't know. But Joe doesn't know whether Frank knows Tokyo.

26   To include the rest of the clause after *whether*.

27   "not to"

28   "Go if you want to, but someone ought to go with you. Shall I ask Gordon to?"

29   No. The umbrella, and the forgetting of it.

30   Yes. Either remove *it* or change *it* to *that*.

31   What Sir Humphrey said.

32   —

33   **e.g.** "He ran well, but not fast enough to win the race."

34   We cannot omit *he* in the subordinate clause.

35   *Because* he worked so much.

36   "A form often used in writing is the non-finite clause."

37   **e.g.** ". . . he finished the race."

38   Drop out *Because*.

39   Yes. Time or reason.

40   *Since* + *-ing* can only denote time. So the credit may not be yours, though circumstantial evidence suggests it is.

UNIT FOURTEEN

Note that the key does not include punctuation marks where it is drawing attention to intonation features.

1   Two: "Penelope dyed her hair green."
"Penelope surprised her friends."

2   The first presents the message as two pieces of information, the second as one. The cook would need to know the difference.

3   **e.g.** "There's a man over there with a gùn."
"There's a màn over there | with a gùn."

4   **e.g.** "Bill's asleèp."

5   **e.g.** "Ĕlephants | have very long mèmories."

6   **e.g.** "I said Bill's asleèp."

7   "He ǎsked her | whether it was pǒssible | to have a cake with a chěrry on it | or nòt."

8   "Classes will begin at ten thìrty." Case (A).

9   "Yesterday morning at ten o'clòck | the rain came down in shèets." Case (B).

10   "Cream cǎkes, | which are fǎttening, | should be avòided." Case (C).

11   "Ànd | to sum úp | we should be careful about what we wèar." Case (D).

12·   "Géorge, | stop pulling your sister's hàir." Case (E).

13 "People who live in the coùntry |
    on the óther hand | are more
    relàxed." Case (E).

14 "Either sǎy something | or stop
    tàlking." Case (G).

15 Grammar. So: ". . . a gràmmar
    book."

16 She's wearing a coat but it isn't
    leather.

17 You thought he drank coffee (or
    something), not tea.

18 "Nò, | Henry the Ěighth | had sìx
    wives." (Mostly temporary.)

19 How they got out again.

20 **e.g.** "whỳ."

21 No. Contrast is with *possible*.

22 **e.g.** "prè-natal care." (Or one
    can say 'ànte-natal').

23 **e.g.** "abòut."

24 —

25 "Alison was telling me . . ."

26 The hour.

27 A sweet thing.

28 Who's speaking.

29 **e.g.** Driving somebody else's.

30 **e.g.** " 'waste mìne."

31 "The phòne's ringing." (What
    else do phones do?)

32 Jack's wrong nucleus placement:
    stand is all it can do in the
    circumstances.

33 Yes.

34 No. Yes.

35 The second.

36 In the first clause.

37 "Brian was hungry when he
    arrǐved."

38 "Brian was hùngry | when he
    arríved."

39 *The police* should be made more
    important.
    e.g. "If you don't remove your
    dǒnkey | I'll have to call the
    polìce."

40 What Long John Silver had on
    his shoulder was a large parrot
    screeching loud obscenities. (We
    are interested in the parrot and
    what he is doing.)

UNIT FIFTEEN

1 Simon is known to us, so he
    comes first.

2 No. In this sentence *The
    professor* is the topic: *a
    completely new topic* is the
    information focus.

3 —

4 When the desserts have been
    served the wrong way round (like
    the sentence).

5 Because it has a fronted
    complement: perfectly
    acceptable, but not very
    common.

6 **e.g.** ". . . his brother Maximǐlian |
    I lòathe."

7 **e.g.** "Spǐders | I'm frìghtened of |
    but bĕetles | are all rìght."

8 **e.g.** "Běautiful | she mày be, | but
    she's not very clěver."

9 **e.g.** "Prǒbably . . . pròmise."

10 —

11 The second.

12   Information (just) given.

13   This I think we can all take for granted.

14   Adverbial fronted to emphasise the struggle.

15   —

16   To give end-focus to *the judge's flag*.

17   "Never/Not . . . will he . . ."

18   For end-focus.

19   End-weight for *the doomed aeroplane*.

20   *Sunned* is transitive, *lay* is not.

21   *Washed* is transitive: this bad order sounds as though *his feet* gave the rest of Norman's body a good scrub-down.

22   *There* does as an adverbial of place.
     Carefully doesn't – it's an adverb of manner.

23   "Down went the starter's flag and away roared the racing cars."

24   Apart from the noise of the cars roaring past, because *it* is a personal pronoun: ". . . away it goes!"

25   The second – more than just an introductory *there* (look over your shoulder!).

26   ". . . was his brother Egbert." Subject-verb inversion after comparative complement.

27   "In no circumstances is war justified."

28   Because subject-operator inversion is obligatory after *Rarely*. Try *did he go* instead of *he went*.

29   Give the first a full stop, the second a question mark.

30   **e.g.** ". . . do I speak as < rhetorically > as this."

31   "Little did Priscilla realise what enormous problems her hasty words would cause."

32   "Only very much later did Holmes discover the truth."

33   In a newspaper caption.

34   He expressed an intention (or prediction) which this speaker shares.

35   Perhaps "My soup was cold."

36   Not Jemima, but some other woman: she too has asked Jemima to come.

37   She is Jemima, and she has come.

38   —

39   —

40   **e.g.** ". . . did he look that we all fell about laughing." "He looked so ridiculous that we all fell about laughing."

UNIT SIXTEEN

1   "No, it's Doris that I want to marry."

2   It was in 1492 that Columbus discovered America.

3   "Eventually, Bob was selected."

4   " – what we want is action."

5   —

6   **e.g.** " – it's fame that I want."/ " – it's glory that I'm after."

7 **e.g.** "... I like to sit and read."

8 "It is there that Shakespeare was born in 1564." or "It is where ..."

9 The first.

10 **e.g.** "No. It was in Regent Street (that there was a riot)."
or: "No. Regent Street was where the riot was."

11 Generally, no. The first gives end focus to *in September* simply as new information. The second gives *in September* contrastive focus.

12 "It was Spike Muggins that (who) pushed the victim to his death."

13 No. Even worse. A simpler sentence would be better.

14 "What he's done is wreck my new car."

15 Mixing his *-ing* and his *to*. "What they're doing is pretending to be innocent."

16 Focus on *discuss politics* as against, for example, *play golf*. Focus on *politics* as against, for example, *the place of structuralism in twentieth century thought*.

17 Three: "No. What he is is a plumber."
"No. A plumber is what he is."
"No. He's a plumber."

18 **e.g.** "What he's done is jumble the sentence." Or simply: "He's jumbled the sentence."

19 **e.g.** "That's why I did it."
"That's what I like."
"This is where I was born."
"That's how she earns her money."

20 The preceding statement, no doubt concerning the need to be visible over long distances and in bad weather.

21 The second, because it ignores the end-weight principle.

22 "That Roger could have committed such a crime is impossible." This focuses on *impossible*.

23 It should be an after-thought, not the focus: "... politícian."

24 **e.g.** "You must find it daunting living with Margaret."

25 *it* = the act of making the decision.
it = something referred to previously, for example an inheritance.

26 "The moment came when Andrew had to decide who his friends were."

27 "The secret agent explained in his own words how he managed to keep silent."

28 —

29 The comparative clause needs postponing.
"Far more cures are available today than used to be the case in the early part of this century."

30 *Turned up* needs to come after *children* as the verb: otherwise, it seems to refer to the retroussé facial feature of the aforementioned puppet.

31 It gives end-focus to *damp*.

32 Because *the police* want end-focus.

33 Yes. "I am delighted that you were able to come after all."

34   A that-clause cannot be the complement of a preposition. But you could get by without the *by*.

35   Personal pronoun objects cannot be moved to the end.

36   Not wrong; but it would come better after *declared*.

37   "Who did Randolph show his stamp collection to?"
     "What did Randolph show the Senator's children?"

38   No. If you give a loud scream, I am unlikely to thank you for it.

39   "Take/Have a rest."
     "Have a drink."

40   —

UNIT SEVENTEEN

1   "... doesn't have any either!"

2   "British Premier Forthright today resigned."

3   Oxford, no doubt. A Harvard student would be at *the* university.

4   No: in America, one would get *his* or *your* deserts (but feminism may soon change this).

5   The Englishman /eɪ/ his.

6   "... haven't finished their part of the job either."

7   The USA's.

8   An American friend.

9   "Did you use(d) to play ...?"

10   Lincolnshire. An American is likely to use *on the weekend*.

11   They watch a ball game (on) Saturdays too: but the game is different.

12   Six days, somewhere in America.

13   In Birmingham, Alabama rather than Birmingham, West Midlands.

14   "While". And a British speaker.

15   No, not by British standards. But some Americans think so.

16   —

17   Yes, for example: "The committee have (or has) decided that the post *should* remain open."

18   Definitely an Englishman, and probably an older person.

19   "You have to be joking."

20   No, Americans don't have to, and the British needn't always.

21   Barbara is probably British and Brenda is probably American.

22   Put a comma after *questions* and another after *know*, surrounding the comment clause.

23   An Englishman, of course.

24   e.g. "It has been agreed that the Company shall have the right to appoint Board members without consulting the shareholders."

25   Ronald, who is American or British, to Margaret, who is British.

26   In the USA.

27   Probably not; they would be more likely to say "Excuse me" or "(I beg your) pardon".

28   e.g. "I beg your pardon. Is anyone serving here?"

29   Maurice: *Well* should introduce a new topic, but he is already talking about the puppy.

Doris: *Now* should add to an established topic, but she introduces a totally new one.

30   Adverbs and adverbials of this kind are used to mark a sequence of logical points, probably in written English.

31   Latin abbreviations don't normally occur in speech.

32   It could sound less formal if it was rewritten like this.

33   An Englishman.

34   A full stop or colon, to give two pieces of information, grammatically independent. No punctuation: it is a grammatical and informational unit.

35   An author is someone who wri̍tes.
An ǎuthor is someone | who writes bo̍oks.
An ǎuthor is someone | who sweats blǒod | to write bo̍oks.
An ǎuthor is someone | who sweats blǒod | to write bo̍oks | which nobody bu̍ys.

36   **e.g.** "The lecturer told the students that, provided they worked hard and paid attention in class, they would all pass."

37   "Nice hat you're wearing."

38   To read it (fronting for negative effect).

39   The first is <formal literary>, the second <informal speech>. Their combination is not unlawful but it is unlikely.

40   "the cleft sentence"

UNIT EIGHTEEN

1   The majority of students shared many problems/had many problems in common.

2   The writer's (or, but not necessarily, the writers').

3   Not necessarily. You may be making a general point.

4   The speaker is not consistently <formal>. Try *for some time.*

5   **e.g.** "They've cancelled a lot of flights because of the weather."

6   "In case"

7   "so"

8   **e.g.** "If there's any trouble, . . ."
"If you have any trouble, . . ."

9   **e.g.** "Mr Sprat cannot eat fat, while his wife is unable to digest lean meat."

10   "anyway"

11   **e.g.** "To what extent . . ."

12   **e.g.** "Do you have something a bit cheaper?"
"Yes, but it's a lot less reliable."

13   **e.g.** "The country needs not only doctors but trained nurses."
or: "It is not only doctors but also trained nurses that the country needs."

14   **e.g.** "Would you mind telling me your age (please)?"

15   **e.g.** "Who are you going with?"

16   **e.g.** "I'm sorry, I missed that. What did you do?"

17   —

18   **e.g.** "If you rephrased this, it would sound . . ."

19   Your neighbour.

20   **e.g.** "I'm rather worried about my wife, Doctor."

21   "May we . . .?" / "Are we allowed to . . .?" / "Could we . . .?" / "Might we . . .?"

22   **e.g.** "I really must be going."

23   **e.g.** <familiar>: "I wouldn't mind some sugar if there is some." <very formal>: "I wonder if you would kindly pass me the sugar."

24   **e.g.** "May I invite you to lunch tomorrow?" "I'm afraid I've already got a lunch appointment."

25   "Entry without pass strictly forbidden."

26   **e.g.** "We undertake to deliver the printed copy within six months of receipt of manuscript."

27   ANN: Good morning, John.
JOHN: Oh, hello, Ann.
ANN: May I introduce you to Professor Nollidge?
JOHN: Very pleased to meet you.

28   No. He should know that a chauffeur and his employer would use consistently <formal> English.

29   **e.g.** Dear Madam,
        I confirm that I wish to be met on arrival off the 12 noon train on Tuesday next.
                        Yours faithfully,
                        J.Miller

or: Dear Miss Brown,
        Would you please arrange to meet me off the 12 noon train next Tuesday.
                        Yours sincerely,
                        Jonathan Miller

30   With great formality (and no doubt regret). **e.g.** "I regret that I am unable to accept this outstanding international honour."

31   No, you give Mort greetings and good wishes from the speaker.

32   —

33   *Incidentally* could become *By the way.*

34   *What's more* could become *Moreover* or *Furthermore.*

35   Keep it < informal> **e.g.** "Sorry, no tomato. But we've got mushroom."

36   **e.g.** ". . . and . . ."

37   "or" or "or else"

38   "Not me!"

39   Non-finite clauses of the -ing type.

40   "this" . . . "that" – and THAT'S THAT!

INDEX

References are to unit and question (e.g. **2.20** = Unit two, question twenty of *Talking About Grammar*).

The conventions are those of *A Communicative Grammar of English*. Grammatical terms are entered in CAPITALS (e.g. ADVERBS). Other subjects and notions appear in ordinary type (e.g. ability). Individual words are printed in *italics* (e.g. *able*).